How to inte

By

R.A. Penfold

BERNARD BABANI (publishing) LTD
THE GRAMPIANS
SHEPHERDS BUSH ROAD
LONDON W6 7NF
ENGLAND

Please Note

Although every care has been taken with the production of this book to ensure that any projects, designs, modifications, and/ or programs, etc. contained herewith, operate in a correct and safe manner and also that any components specified are normally available in Great Britain, the Publisher and Author do not accept responsibility in any way for the failure (including fault in design) of any projects, design, modification, or program to work correctly or to cause damage to any equipment that it may be connected to or used in conjunction with, or in respect of any other damage or injury that may be caused, nor do the Publishers accept responsibility in any way for the failure to obtain specified components.

Notice is also given that if any equipment that is still under warranty is modified in any way or used or connected with home-built equipment then that warranty may be void.

First Published - July 1999

British Library Cataloguing in Publication Data
A catalogue record for this book is available from the British Library

ISBN   0 85934 467 3

Cover Design by Gregor Arthur
Printed and bound in Great Britain by Cox & Wyman Ltd, Reading

Preface

The "PC" is now the standard computer for office use, and it also has a strong following amongst home users and in some niche markets. Specialist hardware add-ons is certainly one of these niche markets, and a PC is the standard choice for scientific, educational, and hobby users who require a computer to form the basis of all sorts of weird and wonderful gadgets. With the right add-on equipment a PC can operate as a weather station, a piece of electronic test gear, the ultimate in model train controllers, or just about anything else. Designing and building your own PC add-ons is not particularly difficult, but the stumbling block for many wannabe add-on builders is the interfacing of the gadget to the PC. How do you actually get the signals into and out of a PC and control your gadgets properly?

A PC can actually interface to your peripheral devices by way of several routes. One of these is via the standard ISA expansion slots, but this is relatively difficult and is not ideal for beginners. This method is well suited to the more advanced user who can tackle double-sided printed circuit boards. Easier options are provided in the form of the standard parallel and serial ports. In this book all three methods are covered in some detail, including tried and tested circuits for any necessary hardware. The software side of things is also covered, including both MS/DOS and Windows programs. With the Windows "visual" approach to programming it is often possible to produce sophisticated control programs for your add-ons that contain remarkably little program code. You certainly do not need to be an expert programmer in order to produce good quality software for your hardware projects.

The risks of damaging a PC by connecting it to your own circuits are probably quite small, especially if you only use the parallel and serial ports. However, it is perhaps worth making the point that most do-it-yourself PC add-ons do not require a powerful PC, and can breathe new life into an old and otherwise unused PC. You can then experiment with PC add-ons more or less risk-free while being environmentally sound!

Robert Penfold

Contents

Chapter 3
PRINTER PORT INTERFACING 83

Chapter 4
SERIAL INTERFACING 121

Chapter 5
SOFTWARE CONSIDERATIONS 151

Appendix
TAPPING OFF POWER 177

Trademarks

Chapter 1

PC BASICS

Some of the popular eight bit computers of the 1980s came equipped with a user port and (or) some sort of expansion port that provided an easy means of connecting do-it-yourself add-ons. Modern 16/32 bit computers are generally somewhat less accommodating. User ports seem to be non-existent on modern computers, and a proper expansion port is by no means a universal feature. Despite this, 16/32 bit machines do have some potential for the electronic hobbyist, scientist, etc., who needs to use a computer in measurement and control applications. The PCs are probably more accommodating in this respect than any other current computer, not that there are that many computers to choose from these days.

There is no true PC equivalent to the user port of eight-bit computers such as the BBC Model B and the Commodore 64. These user ports are basically eight bit parallel ports with each line individually programmable as an input or an output. Additionally there are two handshake lines, plus two sixteen bit timer/counters. This type of port makes it very easy to interface a wide range of circuits to the computer. The nearest PC equivalent to a user port is a parallel input/output card added into one of the expansion slots. Such cards are produced commercially (but can be a bit difficult to track down). They can, of course, be home constructed if you are not daunted by the prospect of tackling do-it-yourself double-sided printed circuit boards.

Slot Machines

The PCs do have something broadly comparable to the expansion ports of the popular eight-bit computers. This is in the form of the vacant expansion slots within the computer, which from the electrical point of view are very similar indeed to traditional expansion ports. Physically they are clearly a rather different proposition. A normal expansion port consists physically of a multi-way connector on the exterior of the computer. Only one add-on at a time can be fitted to the port unless some form of expansion system is used. Normally the add-on simply plugs straight onto the port, or it connects to it via a multi-way cable terminated in a suitable connector. This second method is the one that is generally the easier to implement, and it is the one I tend to favour for do-it-yourself add-ons.

With a PC there is no need for any expansion units to accommodate several user add-ons. With most PCs there are three or more free expansion slots for this type of thing. In the past multi-function cards helped to keep a reasonable number of slots free on computers that had to be well equipped with ports, etc. These days there is usually a fair range of ports provided on the motherboard, and in some cases the sound and video are also provided by the motherboard. This usually leaves several free expansion slots. It is only fair to point out that some PCs, particularly some of the very small types, do not have many free slots once they have been equipped with the bare necessities for normal PC computing. In most examples there are actually several free slots, but for one reason or another they are mostly inaccessible. If you are interested in do-it-yourself PC interfacing there is a lot to be said for a traditional PC case and motherboard, with lots of free slots and space inside the case.

Having the add-on cards inside the computer has its advantages and drawbacks. On the plus side, there is no need to worry about connecting cables getting broken. Neither is there a problem with units fitted on the back of the computer getting in the way, or becoming accidentally detached. Units that mount direct onto expansion ports at the rear of computers are notorious for crashing the computer if they should be accidentally knocked. In the past there were one or two units of this type that had a reputation for crashing the computer if you should happen to breathe too hard near them! With the cards mounted securely inside the computer there is no real problem with unreliability even if the computer should take a few knocks.

The main drawback from the do-it-yourself point of view is that any add-on circuit must be on an accurate double-sided printed circuit board of irregular shape. This should be fitted with a metal mounting bracket so that the board can be firmly bolted in place. Unfortunately, the metal mounting bracket has a fairly elaborate shape that makes it a bit tricky for home construction. Connections to the outside world are via connectors mounted at the rear edge of the printed circuit board.

In order to tackle this type of thing you need to have a fair amount of experience at electronics construction, and a fair degree of expertise. There are ways of making things a little easier though. If you do not feel competent to etch and drill your own double-sided printed circuit boards, or simply do not have the necessary facilities to handle this type of thing, there are companies that can produce prototype boards if you can provide them with reasonable artwork for the board design. However, having one-off boards made can be quite expensive. Whether or not this method is practical depends on how much you are prepared to pay, and on what sort of deal you can negotiate with a printed circuit manufacturing company. For this type of thing a small company is likely to be a better bet than one which normally produces a few thousand boards at a time.

Proprietary Cards
An alternative approach is to use a proprietary printed circuit board rather than a custom type. Ordinary stripboards, etc., are not much use in this context, where a double-sided edge connector is needed to make the connections to an expansion slot. It is actually possible to make up an edge connector to fit an expansion slot, and to fit this onto a piece of stripboard. The edge connector should be fitted with pins so that you can easily

3

make connections from the connector/slot to the stripboard. In theory you can easily make up prototype circuits on the stripboard, and wire them to the expansion slot. The system is reusable in that fresh pieces of stripboard can be fitted to the new connector when new circuits must be developed. Connections to the outside world can be made via a connector fitted on the stripboard, or by way of a flying lead (the latter probably representing the more practical solution).

While this all sounds fine in theory, and will work to some extent in practice, it is a method that I have found to be less than perfect. The main problem is that modern stripboard is not particularly tough, and in fairness it must be said that it is not intended for this type of use. This method tends to be frustrating and expensive, as the stripboard tends to break at the join with the edge connector. If you decide to adopt this method you therefore need to proceed with caution, and must treat the board/connector assembly with the proverbial "kid gloves". This method has to be regarded as considerably less than ideal for either prototyping purposes or finished cards.

What is probably a better approach is to use one of the proprietary prototyping cards which are specifically designed for PC prototyping (but which are also suitable for final units). A slight problem with these is that they do not seem to be very widely available in the U.K., but they are available from a few of the larger electronic component retailers. Unfortunately, those that are available tend to be quite expensive. They vary in sophistication from simple double-sided boards with no electronics, through to boards which have buffers, an address decoder, breadboards, etc. For most do-it-yourself enthusiasts only the simple boards are a practical proposition, as anything beyond this tends to be prohibitively expensive. Even simple prototyping boards tend to cost much more than stripboard, etc., of a similar size, but they are usually high quality fibreglass boards. In view of this, I suppose that they actually offer quite good value for money.

4

DIY Prototype Cards

Of course, it is quite possible to build for yourself something comparable to these ready made prototyping cards. However, I think that even if you were fairly expert at making double-sided printed circuit boards it would be necessary to settle for a simplified version of a proprietary board. One problem is simply that it could take weeks to manually drill the thousands of holes in one of these cards! Having the holes through plated is useful, but is probably not something for the do-it-yourself board maker to bother with.

An approach to home produced prototype boards that I have found useful is to have an edge connector which does not have any pads connecting to terminals that will, in all probability, never be needed for any of your prototype circuits. The functions of the terminals on the edge connector, plus their relative importance, is something that will be discussed more fully later in this chapter. However, it is fair to say that less than half of these terminals actually need to be used for most do-it-yourself expansion cards. Leaving out some of the "fingers" of the edge connector does not actually simplify things very much, but not having to bother with tracks and pads to connect to them can help simplify things a great deal.

On the main part of the board it is probably best to settle for some DIL clusters to take integrated circuits, including one or two 40 pin types to accommodate the larger integrated circuits which are a feature of so many computer add-ons. Remember that if you use 20 and 40 pin clusters, between them these will also accommodate most other sizes of integrated circuit, albeit with some pads left unused. Each pad of each cluster can connect to a row of pads, and some rows of stripboard style pads can be used to provide a general prototyping area for discrete component amplifiers, oscillators, or whatever. Even using this approach there will be a large number of holes to drill, but nothing like as many as would be needed if the entire board were covered with holes on a 0.1-inch matrix. You can actually eliminate most of the hole drilling by leaving the main part of the board blank. You can then bolt onto this area a piece of stripboard, or any form of general-purpose prototyping board. This includes solderless breadboards, which are perfectly suitable for most PC prototype circuits (but which are obviously not really appropriate to finished units). A card of this type enables new circuits to be rapidly checked and (hopefully) perfected, and can be used over and over again.

For the ultimate in convenience when PC prototyping you can build a card along the lines just described, but include an address decoder on the card. This avoids having to make up an address decoder each time you test a new circuit, and keeps things as quick and simple as possible. This is certainly the type of prototyping card I favour, and is the one I normally use when checking PC prototype circuits. Ideally the address decoder should have several outputs representing different address ranges, or it should be switchable between several address ranges. This enables prototype circuits to be set so that they will not conflict with any user add-ons already in the computer. Address decoding is discussed later in this book.

A variation on this theme is to add an address decoder onto a proprietary PC prototyping card. Connect pins to the pads that connect to important terminals of the edge connector so that connections can be easily made to these lines. If you do not like the idea of prototyping circuits direct onto the board, simply fit it with stripboard, a couple of breadboards, or whatever. This arrangement gives you a very versatile prototyping system, and avoids the need to make up a difficult double-sided printed circuit board. I suppose that you could even make up finished circuits on stripboard or some similar proprietary board, mount

6

it on a ready made PC prototyping card and then wire it to the edge connector. This would not give the neatest of results, but it should work well enough in practice.

If you require the simplest means of PC interfacing, the obvious approach is to have an edge connector to fit the expansion bus, with a ribbon cable connected to this. Your add-on circuits can then be connected to the opposite end of this cable, and situated outside the PC. They can be breadboarded, constructed on stripboard, or built using any desired method. This is the PC equivalent to the method used for most do-it-yourself add-ons for eight bit computers. Unfortunately, in my experience at any rate, this system has proved to be a bit unreliable when applied to PC add-ons. The problem is presumably due to the higher clock frequencies used for PCs, especially the "turbo" PCs that are now the norm.

It would be wrong to say that this method is totally impractical, but it can be difficult to get it to work reliably in practice. The chances of it working with a long connecting cable are small, and the shorter the cable, the better the chances of success. The slower the bus speed the greater the chances of reliable operation. Some computers have a "jumper" on the motherboard that can be used to select a slow or a fast expansion bus clock frequency. With modern PCs there may be a setting or settings in the ROM BIOS Setup program that provide some degree of control over the expansion bus timing. With some computers, especially the old XT variety, the expansion bus speed is dependent on the main system clock frequency. Switching from the "turbo" mode to the normal one will then slow down the expansion bus. You may have both options available, permitting a very slow expansion bus speed if the normal system clock and slow bus clock frequencies are selected. However, bear in mind that by slowing down the system clock and (or) expansion bus you will obtain a general reduction in performance. There is no harm in giving this method of interfacing a try, but if it fails to give reliable results the best option is probably to abandon it in favour of some other method.

The Expansion Buses

Many aspects of PC computing have developed substantially over the years, and the expansion bus is no exception. The original PC/XT bus is an eight-bit type. This may seem strange, since the PCs are sixteen and 32-bit computers. However, the 8088 microprocessor used in the original PCs (and many "clones") is a so-called "cut down" version of the 8086 microprocessor. This basically just means that it has an eight-bit data bus and must take in data and output it eight bits at a time. Operations on sixteen bit chunks of data must therefore be accomplished using two eight-bit instructions rather than a single 16-bit instruction. Once data is inside the microprocessor's internal registers it is handled as sixteen bit chunks, and internally the 8088 is a true sixteen bit microprocessor. This gives some speed disadvantage compared to the 8086, but the speed difference in practical applications is not very large. Although the 8088 has an eight bit bus, because it is a proper sixteen bit component in other respects, the PCs that are based on this chip are usually regarded as sixteen bit machines rather than superior eight bit types.

It is perhaps worth mentioning that some XT class PCs do actually have an 8086 microprocessor. Despite this, they usually retain the standard eight-bit expansion bus in order to give full compatibility with 8088 based XT type PCs. Not many PCs based on the 8086 have been produced, and certain Olivetti and Amstrad PCs are probably the only examples of popular PCs of this type. As far as interfacing 8086 based PCs is concerned, they normally have a fully standard XT type expansion bus, and are therefore interfaced in exactly the same manner as any other XT class PCs.

The first development of the PC expansion bus was the 16-bit type. This became necessary when AT (advanced technology) PCs came along. The have an 80286 microprocessor, which is a full 16-bit type, complete with a 16-bit data bus. Presumably it would have been possible to have an ordinary eight-bit expansion bus on these computers, but it would have removed some of the potential advantages of using the 80286. The solution was to retain the standard eight bit bus, but to augment it with some further lines carried on a second edge connector mounted in front of the existing connector. This enables appropriate 8 bit cards to be used with an AT computer, but still enables sixteen bit cards to be used where these offer advantages. This 16-bit PC expansion bus is often called the "ISA" bus, and "ISA" simply stands for "Industry Standard Architecture".

Note that PC compatibles that are based on the 80386SX 16-bit microprocessor are basically just AT computers, and are interfaced in the same way. Similarly, PCs that are based on the 80386, 80486SX, and 80486 32-bit microprocessors are essentially AT type PCs. They do usually have a 32-bit expansion bus, but in most cases only one slot is of this type. It is normally in the form of a standard 16-bit PC expansion bus with an extra edge connector mounted in front. This added edge connector carries the extra lines needed for 32-bit interfacing. There is no true standard for these 32-bit slots though, and they normally only accept memory expansion cards produced specially for each make of computer. These 32-bit expansion buses are now long obsolete anyway, and are something that will not be considered further here.

There is actually a standard 32-bit PC expansion bus, which is the result of agreements between several major manufacturers of PC compatibles. This is the "EISA" ("Extended Industry Standard Architecture") bus. From the physical point of view this is substantially different to the 32-bit expansion buses of ISA 80386 and 80486 PCs. It has the normal ISA bus, but an extra connector alongside this provides the additional lines needed for 32-bit interfacing. It is a high speed bus which has definite advantages over the standard ISA bus for advanced applications that genuinely require very high speed data transfers. However, for many purposes, including most user add-on applications, the ordinary ISA bus will suffice. The EISA bus is not something we will pursue further here.

There is a fourth type of PC expansion bus, and this is IBM's MCA (Micro Channel Architecture) bus. This is another high-speed 32-bit type, and is one that is used on the more advanced of IBM's recent PCs. These computers are not really traditional PCs, and are intended to be a sort of new generation of PCs. While they have good software compatibility with ordinary PCs, they are largely incompatible as far as hardware is concerned. Consequently, interfacing to this type of PC really falls outside the scope of this book.

Finally, modern PCs are equipped with several PCI slots that replace some of the ISA expansion slots. The PCI slots offer definite advantages over the ISA type, such as higher operating speed, 32/64 operation, and full "plug and play" support. In the fullness of time PCI slots will totally replace the ISA variety, but as yet I have not encountered a PC that has less than two ISA slots. Unfortunately, interfacing via the PCI bus seems to be extremely complex, and it would not appear to support any form of basic interfacing suitable for DIY add-ons. Using the PCI bus is certainly well beyond the scope of the present publication.

Although modern PCs are based on Pentium or equivalent processors, they are still essentially AT "clones", and provided they have the standard ports they can be interfaced to the outside world in much the same way as the original PCs. Most of the information in this book therefore applies equally to an old PC XT clone, a modern Pentium II PC, and anything in between.

The ISA Bus
The ISA bus has a two by 31-way 0.1-inch pitch edge connector to carry the basic eight-bit section of the bus. The female

connectors are on the computer's motherboard, while the add-on cards must have a male edge connector. This male edge connector is basically just a protrusion on the card, which has the 31 "fingers" of copper on both sides of the board. The extra lines for 16-bit interfacing are carried by a two by 18-way edge connector mounted in front of the two by 31-way connector. Figure 1.1 gives details of this arrangement, including the standard method of pin numbering used for both connectors.

This is a list of the the eight-bit expansion bus lines:

Terminal No.	Function
A1	-I/O CH CK
A2	D7
A3	D6
A4	D5
A5	D4
A6	D3
A7	D2
A8	D1
A9	D0
A10	I/O CH RDY
A11	AEN
A12	A19
A13	A18
A14	A17
A15	A16
A16	A15
A17	A14
A18	A13
A19	A12
A20	A11
A21	A10
A22	A9
A23	A8
A24	A7
A25	A6

A26	A5
A27	A4
A28	A3
A29	A2
A30	A1
A31	A0
B1	GND
B2	RESET
B3	+5V
B4	IRQ2
B5	−5V
B6	DRQ2
B7	−12V
B8	Reserved
B9	+12V
B10	GND
B11	-MEMW
B12	-MEMR
B13	-IOW
B14	-OR
B15	-DACK3
B16	DRQ3
B17	-DACK1
B18	DRQ1
B19	-DACK0
B20	CLK
B21	IRQ7
B22	IRQ6
B23	IRQ5
B24	IRQ4
B25	IRQ3
B26	-DACK2
B27	TC
B28	ALE
B29	+5V
B30	OSC
B31	GND

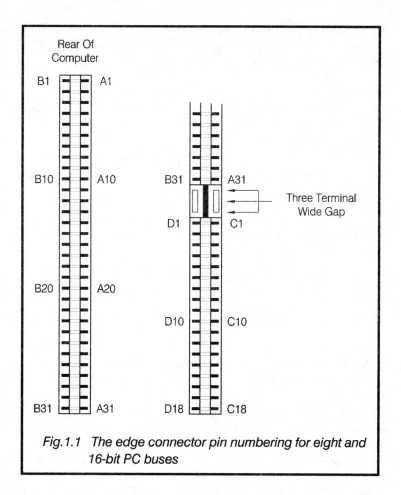

Fig.1.1 *The edge connector pin numbering for eight and 16-bit PC buses*

(A minus sign at the beginning of a function description indicates that the line is negative active).

Many of these lines will be familiar to anyone who has undertaken interfacing on eight bit computers, and should be particularly familiar to anyone who has dealt with computers based on the 8080 or Z80 microprocessors. However, for the benefit of those who have limited experience of computer interfacing a description of each line (or set of lines) is provided in the following sections.

Data/Address Bus
Lines D0 to D7 are the standard eight-bit bidirectional data bus. Any data provided by your add-on circuits is fed into the microprocessor via these eight lines. Similarly, any data fed from the microprocessor to your add-on circuits will come by way of these eight lines. A0 to A19 are the address bus, and are outputs provided by the microprocessor. These provide a one-megabyte address range for memory circuits. 16 and 32-bit PCs have additional address lines on the second edge connector which enables a much larger amount of memory to be accommodated. However, PCs, which have 16 or 32-bit microprocessors normally operate in an 8088 emulation mode where only the basic 20-bit address bus is utilized. These days increasing use of the extended memory of 16 and 32-bit machines is made via disc caches, DOS extenders, etc. This is largely of academic importance to the do-it-yourself add-on enthusiast, and you will normally only need address lines A0 to A19. In fact you will not normally deal with interfacing memory circuits, and will not even require all these address lines.

The address bus is also used for selecting the correct input/output circuit. In this context only the lower 16 lines (A0 to A15) are utilized. This gives some 64K of input/output address space, or some 65536 input/output addresses in other words. This is more than would ever be needed in a real computer system, and a somewhat simplified approach has therefore been used on the PCs. Only the lower ten address lines (A0 to A9) are utilized, which still gives some 1024 usable input/output addresses. The lower half of the address range is reserved for internal use (i.e. circuits on the motherboard), leaving the upper 512 addresses free for expansion cards. Many of these addresses are reserved for specific functions, such as the standard ports and disc controllers. There is still plenty of space left for your own expansion cards. The input/output map is a topic we will discuss fully later on.

Control Bus

The 8088 microprocessor has a control bus that consists of seven lines. Four of these are MEMR, MEMW, IOR, and IOW, which are all forms of read/write line. Unlike some microprocessors, the 8088 has separate read and write lines, not one line that indicates one type of operation when set high, and the opposite type when set low. Also, the 8088 has separate memory and input/output maps. 8088 based computers do not have input/output devices placed at empty spaces in the memory map, as do computers based on chips such as the 6502 and 68000. Thus, what is a single control line on some microprocessors become some four lines on the 8088 series. These lines are all active low. MEMR goes low when the microprocessor is reading from memory - MEMW goes low when it is writing to memory. IOR is activated when data is read from an input device - IOW is activated when data is written to an output circuit. These are obviously important lines that will often have to be decoded by your add-on circuits. Presumably any do-it-yourself add-on cards will not fit in the memory map, but will go into the input/output map. Accordingly, you will not normally need to bother with MEMR and MEMW, but will need to use IOR and IOW extensively.

ALE (address latch enable) is a control line that can be used to synchronise events to microprocessor bus cycles. This is not a line that you will normally need to bother with. The same is not true of AEN (address enable) which goes low during processor bus cycles (i.e. normal operations). It is needed to distinguish between normal bus cycles and DMA (direct memory access) cycles. This must be decoded to the low state by the address/control bus decoder.

The reset line is an output generated by the computer, which is a standard active high reset line. This goes high at switch on, or if there is a hardware reset (i.e. if you press the computer's

15

reset button). Software resets, which includes those produced using the keyboard Control - Alt - Delete sequence, do not normally result in a reset signal being produced on the reset line. It is not essential to use this line to provide the reset signal for your add-on circuits. Some may simply not require a reset signal at all, while with others it might be easier to include a reset pulse generator circuit on the expansion card. In most cases though, where a reset signal is needed it is probably easier to use the computer's reset line. If a negative active reset signal is needed, simply feeding the reset line of the expansion port through an inverter should provide a suitable signal.

DMA/Interrupts

There are nine DMA lines. DACK0 to DACK3 are outputs, as is the TC (terminal count) line. DIRQ1 to DIRQ4 are inputs. These are lines that are only needed for circuits which make use of the advanced DMA facilities. This is not likely to include home constructed expansion cards, and we will consequently not consider the DMA lines further here.

The 8088 has eight normal interrupt lines of the active high variety, but IRQ0 and IRQ1 are not available on the expansion bus. Neither are the special (high priority) interrupt lines such as NMI (non-maskable interrupt). Interrupt lines IRQ2 to IRQ7 are available, but bear in mind that standard expansion cards such as the serial and parallel ports will use some of these. For most user add-ons there is no need to utilize the interrupt lines, but they can be useful where it is important that the computer responds to the add-on very rapidly. Applications of this type are usually where data must be read intermittently, but when the data does come along, it does so in large quantities and at a high rate. It is important that each byte of data is read very soon after it has been received, or it may be over-written by the next byte of data. Using the interrupt lines on any computer is a fairly complex business though, and it is much easier to crash the computer than to get it right. Using interrupts on the PCs is perhaps a little less fraught than using interrupts on some of the popular eight bit computers. Even so, this is something that is strictly for the advanced user.

Power and Clocks
The expansion bus includes two clock lines. OSC is a buffered crystal controlled oscillator signal at 14.318MHz. It is mainly included to act as the clock signal for the colour graphics adaptor, and it is probably not of much use for anything else. The other clock signal is CLK, which is the system clock, which has a two to one duty cycle. For the original PCs the system clock was at 4.77MHz, but on most PC XT "clones" it is normally 8MHz, 10MHz, or even higher. On AT class computers the clock frequency can be practically anything from 6MHz to 450MHz. AT type PCs used to have the ability to operate at a "normal" clock frequency of about 8MHz, and a "turbo" mode of around 20MHz to 50MHz (4.77MHz and about 8MHz to 15MHz for XT class PCs). With Pentium PCs the "turbo" switch is normally absent (or present but it does not actually do anything), and the computer always operates at its maximum clock frequency.

Clearly the system clock signal can not be relied upon to be at a certain frequency. On AT computers it may well be missing, with no connection made to this terminal of the expansion bus. These factors must be borne in mind when designing an interface that uses this clock signal. Of course, if you are only producing a card for your own use in a computer where this clock signal is present, and will always be at a certain frequency, then you can design the card on the basis of a known and reliable clock frequency. Remember though, that if you change to a different PC you may have to modify the card in order to get it to function correctly with the new computer. In general it is better to simply ignore both the clock signals on the expansion bus, and where necessary include a suitable clock generator on the expansion card.

Four power supplies plus the 0 volt earth (ground) rail are available on the expansion bus. The available voltages are +5V,

–5V, +12V, and –12V. The +5 volt rail should be able to supply several amps without any problems with overloading. It is difficult to be precise about how much power is available on this line as it depends on the rating of the power supply unit, and the current drawn by the motherboard, expansion cards, etc. Some PCs have massive power supplies and hardware that has very modest power requirements. With these there is likely to be well over ten amps of spare current available.

At the other end of the spectrum there are mini-PCs which have relatively low power supply units, and which might have as little as an amp or two to spare for your add-ons. Since your cards are not likely to consume a total of even one amp of current, any PC should be able to power your add-ons without any difficulty. However, it is probably best to use the PC's supply unit only for electronics. If you are using the PC to control electric motors, filament bulbs, etc., then these should have a separate power supply unit.

The +12 volt supply should also be able to provide an amp or two without any problems. In fact it might be possible to draw as much as 4 amps from the +12 volt line, but it is probably best to stick to a maximum of about 2 amps unless you can definitely ascertain that your computer can reliably supply more than this. On many PCs the +12 volt supply does not seem to be well stabilised, and often seems to be at around +13 volts. I think that I am right in stating that this supply is mainly intended for powering the motors in the disc drives, and that the latter include their own regulator circuits. It is probably not safe to assume that this line is well stabilised, or particularly noise-free.

The ratings of the negative supplies are relatively small. The –5 volt and –12 volt lines are usually rated at 0.3 amps and 0.25 amps respectively (some of which may well be consumed by other cards). It is probably best to keep the current drains from the negative supplies down to about 100 milliamps (0.1 amps) or less. In most applications the negative supplies will not be needed at all, and where they are required it will often only be necessary to draw currents of a few milliamps or less. For example, the "tail" resistor of some analogue to digital converters requires a negative supply current of well under 1 milliamp, and for a circuit that has three or four operational amplifiers a negative supply current of less that 10 milliamps would normally be needed.

The Rest
The IO CH RDY (Input/Output Channel Ready) line is an important one. It is an input that can be used to insert wait states. A wait state is simply a system clock cycle during a read or write operation where nothing happens. The purpose of introducing these "dummy" clock cycles is to slow down the computer to the point where a slow memory or input/output circuit can keep up. This might be necessary for some user add-ons. However, if at all possible it is obviously better to keep things simple by having add-on circuits that can keep up with the computer. In most cases there is no difficulty in doing this, and IO CH RDY can be ignored.

IO CHCK (Input/Output Channel Check) is an active low input line. It is taken low in order to indicate that a memory or input/output parity error has occurred. A non-maskable interrupt is then generated. This line is not normally used with user add-ons.

Sixteen Bit Bus
Most do-it-yourself PC interfacing only requires the eight bit bus, but I suppose that there are some applications which would benefit from use of the full sixteen bit bus. This is a list of the extra functions available on the 16-bit ISA bus.

Terminal No.	Function
D1	-MEM CS16
D2	-I/O CS16
D3	IRQ16

D4	IRQ11
D5	IRQ12
D6	IRQ15
D7	IRQ14
D8	-DACK0
D9	DRQ0
D10	-DAQ10
D11	DRQ5
D12	-DACK6
D13	DRQ6
D14	-DACK7
D15	DRQ7
D16	+5V
D17	-MASTER
D18	GND
C1	BHE
C2	A23
C3	A22
C4	A21
C5	A20
C6	A19
C7	A18
C8	A17
C9	-MEMR
C10	-MEMW
C11	D8
C12	D9
C13	D10
C14	D11
C15	D12
C16	D13
C17	D14
C18	D15

(A minus sign at the beginning of a function description indicates that the line is negative active).

When a PC is equipped with a 16-bit bus there are actually a few changes to the basic eight-bit bus. -DACK0 for instance, becomes -REFRESH on the 16-bit bus. -REFRESH simply indicates that a memory refresh cycle is in progress. This is really only of academic importance since it is highly unlikely that you would ever use one of the lines which is subject to these variations of usage. Most of the extra lines on the 16-bit bus are of no interest to the do-it-yourself interfacing enthusiast. The extra address lines are only needed when accessing extended memory, and are irrelevant to input/output devices. Most of the other lines are interrupt and DMA lines, etc., which you will probably not need to use either.

Of course, the extra data lines (D8 to D15) will be needed for sixteen bit interfacing, and permit data to be exchanged in sixteen bit words rather than being limited to eight bit bytes. BHE is the Bus High Enable output, and it is alternatively known as SBHE (System Bus High Enable). It indicates that data transfer is to be on the high byte (D8 to D15), as well as on the low byte (D0 to D7). Data transfers always involve the lower byte, and so there is no equivalent to this on the eight-bit bus. -MEM CS16 and -I/O CS16 are inputs that are used to inform the computer that memory and input/output data exchanges are to be sixteen bit types. If suitable signals are not applied to these inputs, sixteen bit data transfers will be carried out as two eight bit transfers.

Important Lines
Clearly a large number of the lines included on the expansion bus will not be needed for most interfacing. The terminals of the edge connector that connect to unused lines can obviously be omitted. This can help to simplify the printed circuit boards if you are using custom printed circuit boards. It can massively simplify things if you are making up your own prototyping boards. This is a list of the terminals of the edge connector that you will often need to implement, and which should certainly be included in PC prototyping systems.

Terminal	Function
A2	D7
A3	D6
A4	D5
A5	D4
A6	D3
A7	D2
A8	D1
A9	D0
A11	AEN
A22	A9
A23	A8
A24	A7
A25	A6
A26	A5
A27	A4
A28	A3
A29	A2
A30	A1
A31	A0
B1	0V (GND)
B2	RESET
B3	+5V
B5	−5V
B7	−12V
B9	+12V
B13	-IOW
B14	-IOR

This list is basically just the lower ten lines of the address bus, the data bus, the supply lines, RESET, -IOW and -IOR. For 16-bit interfacing you will normally need these lines as well.

Terminal	Function
D2	-I/O CS16
C1	BHE
C11	D8

C12	D9
C13	D10
C14	D11
C15	D12
C16	D13
C17	D14
C18	D15

Getting Physical

An important aspect of PC interfacing is to get the physical dimensions of the cards spot-on. This is every bit as important as getting things right electronically. Make small errors in certain dimensions and you could find that the card would simply not fit into the computer. Make the edge connector inaccurately and it may well short circuit adjacent pairs of contacts from one end of the expansion slot to the other! This might not actually do any damage to the computer, since most logic circuits are pretty tough, and PC power supplies have comprehensive protection circuits, which should avoid catastrophe in the event of short circuits. However, with this type of thing it is best not to find out the hard way. If your PC should prove to be unable to withstand this type of problem, the result could be an extremely expensive repair bill. When undertaking any computer interfacing it is important to proceed very carefully indeed, taking as few risks as possible. The more expensive the computer, the more carefully you need to proceed.

I prefer not to try out prototype cards on my main PCs at all, but instead use a PC that is largely comprised of left-overs from upgrades to my main PCs, plus parts obtained cheaply at computer fairs or in swaps with friends. This PC is good enough for most PC interfacing applications, and if it should come to a "sticky" end it would be unfortunate, but not a substantial loss. A major repair such as fitting a new motherboard would be an unwelcome expense, but it would not "break the bank". I could not say the same of a repair to something like a 450MHz Pentium II based PC with the latest in future-proofed motherboards.

Interfacing to PCs is certainly something I would not recommend for beginners at electronics. For beginners the best advice is to gain some experience building up a few simple electronic projects before trying your hand at any form of computer interfacing. Then start with some projects that interface to a serial or parallel port. Either that or you should be prepared to write-off your PC against experience!

Physical details of eight and 16-bit cards are shown in Figures 1.2 and 1.3 respectively. These are largely self explanatory, but there are a few important points to note. Firstly, the length dimension given for the cards is for full-length cards. Obviously cards do not have to be full-length types, and probably most PC expansion cards are only about half-length or less. There is no minimum acceptable size for PC cards, but there is a practical limitation in that the card must be long enough to include the full edge connector, or both connectors in the case of a 16-bit card. Of course, if a card is less than full length, it is the front part of the card that is cut down to size. The edge connector and mounting bracket at the rear of the card make it unacceptable to shorten this end. It is probably not a good idea to produce cards that are just fractionally less than full length. It would seem to be better to make such cards full length, so that the guide rails in the computer properly support the front end of the card.

PC expansion cards are generally about 100 millimetres (4 inches) high, excluding the edge connector. With most computers it is safe to have cards of up to about 4.2 inches in height, but above this you may find the card will fit alright, but that the lid of the case can not be closed properly. With some mini PC cases it is necessary to have cards no more than about 4 inches high. There is no minimum height for PC cards, but there are again practical limitations. If you make cards much less than 100 millimetres high it may be very difficult to slot them in place and to remove them again. I generally make PC expansion cards 100 millimetres high and a minimum of about

24

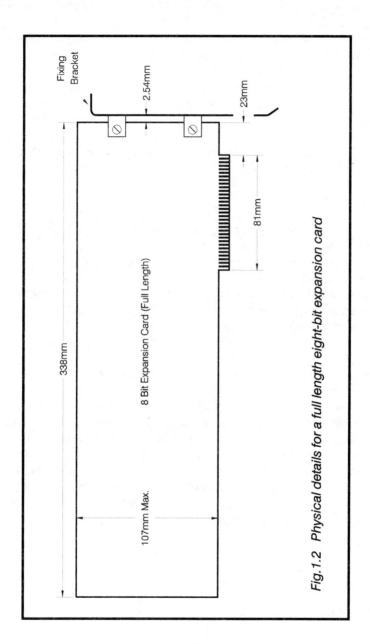

Fig. 1.2 Physical details for a full length eight-bit expansion card

125 millimetres long, even if this gives an area that is far larger than the interface circuit really requires.

Making your own fixing brackets is a bit tricky as they have a quite intricate shape. I will not give any details of fixing brackets here, as the best route to making your own is to copy a blanking plate from one of the expansion slots in your PC. You might actually have one or two spare blanking plates, where these plates have been removed to make way for added expansion cards. Unfortunately, modern cases often have blanking plates that are simply broken away from the case when they are not required, rather than the type that is released via a fixing screw. These are likely to be of little help. Where it is possible to obtain "proper" blanking plates it will almost certainly be easier to use these for your home constructed cards than to try making your own brackets. Of course, a fixing bracket is not absolutely essential, and PC cards fit quite firmly into the expansion slots. If the bracket is omitted it is unlikely that the card will be pulled out of place provided you take reasonable care. It is clearly preferable to include mounting brackets, but many constructors of PC expansion cards prefer to simply omit them altogether. I must admit that I avoid using them whenever possible.

Although in Figures 1.2 and 1.3 the mounting brackets are shown as being fitted to the boards via simple right-angled brackets, these brackets are often unnecessary. Often PC cards are fitted with right angled D connectors to permit connections to be made to the outside world. In such cases the D connectors will normally provide a convenient means of fixing the mounting bracket to the board. A suitable cutout for the connector must be made in the bracket, and this can be cut using a miniature file or a coping saw.

If you are lucky, you may already have one or two brackets which have cut-outs for one or two D connectors. Multi-function cards are often supplied with brackets of this type. These cards often require more sockets than it is possible to accommodate

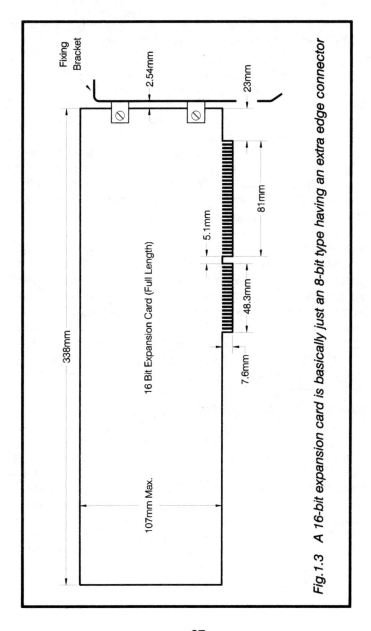

Fig.1.3 A 16-bit expansion card is basically just an 8-bit type having an extra edge connector

on the rear section of the card. The extra sockets must therefore be mounted on blanking plates for unused expansion slots, and connected to the card via jumper leads. Many PC cases have mounting holes for D connectors in the rear panel of the case. You can then use these instead of the drilled blanking plates, leaving the latter free for use with your own expansion cards. If you make your own mounting brackets, unless you have access to some advanced metal working facilities it will be much easier to use thin (about 18 s.w.g.) aluminium than heavy gauge steel. Whatever means you adopt for mounting the bracket on the expansion card make sure that it is the correct distance from the rear of the card. Small errors here can make it impossible to fit the card into the computer.

Programming

The hardware of a PC is normally handled via DOS routines or Windows drivers, but your home constructed expansion cards will usually be types that have no DOS or Windows support. Your only means of reading from them or writing data to them is to directly access the hardware via a suitable programming language. Some languages are better for this type of thing than are others. It is only fair to point out that some PC languages in their raw state are of no use whatever in this context. They simply do not provide instructions that give direct access to devices in the input/output map.

Obviously there should be no problem when using assembly language or machine code since you have direct access to the instructions of the microprocessor which access the input and output circuits. Some computer languages enable programs to call and run assembly language routines, and this provides a means of controlling user add-ons. This method of handling things is much used with eight bit computers running interpreted BASICs. These languages almost invariably provide instructions that can be used to control user add-ons, but for some applications they would simply run too slowly. A mixture of BASIC and assembly language give the convenience of the former, with the speed of the latter when required. This is a system that I have always found to be very good in practice, but the speed of compiled BASICs for 16/32 bit computers tends to make it less attractive in a PC context. However, it is an approach that could be well suited to some situations, and it is certainly something worth keeping in mind.

The BASIC supplied with most PC compatibles in the past was Microsoft's GW BASIC, which is an interpreted BASIC. This was later replaced with a modernised but largely compatible programming language called QBASIC, which is also an interpreted language. This makes GW BASIC and QBASIC easy to use, but they are not fast by PC language standards. On most PCs they are good enough for many applications though, and they are languages I would certainly recommend when initially experimenting with PC add-ons. The speed of modern PCs is such that you can often do things with an interpreted language that would have required a compiled language with early PCs. In GW BASIC or QBASIC the OUT instruction is used to write data to devices in the input/output map (e.g. OUT 768,12 would write a value of 12 to output address 768). Data can be read from devices in the input/output map using the INP function. For instance, the instruction X = INP(768) would set variable X at the value read from input address 768.

Most other BASICs, whether interpreted or compiled, should work perfectly well with user add-ons. The only exceptions are some of the higher level BASICs, which have mouse support, windowing facilities, etc. These often lack facilities for direct accessing of the hardware. Microsoft's Visual BASIC is a good example of a PC BASIC in this category. It would presumably be possible to control the hardware directly via a suitable add-on routine, but INP, OUT, or any equivalent instructions are not supported. A traditional BASIC would seem to be a safer bet than a modern type in the current context. I sometimes get enquiries from users of Windows 95/98 who wish to know where they can obtain either QBASIC or GW BASIC. This is not loaded as part of the "typical" installation option, but it is present on the Windows 95 and 98 CD-ROMs. In the Windows 98 upgrade CD for example, it is in the tools\oldmsdos subdirectory. Note that both QBASIC and GW BASIC are MS/DOS programs. In order to run them under Windows 95 or 98 the computer must be rebooted in MS/DOS mode, or an MS/DOS window must be used.

The abilities of other PC languages to control the computer's hardware seem to vary considerably. Most languages can actually manage this type of thing, but not necessarily in a particularly straightforward manner. If you are not an expert programmer it is probably best to use a good BASIC language. BASIC is a much-maligned language, but any fairly recent version should offer excellent facilities and reasonably fast operating speed. While BASIC is not well suited to all applications, it is very good indeed for measurement and control applications. It is therefore well suited to most applications that involve user add-ons.

Properly Addressed
As explained previously, the input/output map for PCs consists of only 1024 addresses, because only the bottom ten address lines are used for input/output mapping. The lower half of the map is reserved for system hardware (i.e. circuits on the motherboard), while the upper half is reserved for the expansion bus. Standard circuits such as serial and parallel ports do not count as system hardware, since they fit onto the expansion bus (or they did in the original PCs anyway). This means that the 512 address range for the expansion bus is fairly crowded, with few gaps. This is the PC input/output map.

System

Hex Address Range	Function
000-01F	DMA Controller #1
020-03F	Interrupt Controller #1
040-05F	8254 Timer
060-06F	Keyboard Interface
070-07F	Real Time Clock
080-09F	DMA Page Register
0A0-0BF	Interrupt Controller #2
0C0-0DF	DMA Controller #2
0F0	Clear Processor Busy
0F1	Reset Processor
0F8 - 0FF	Arithmetic Processor

Expansion Bus

Hex Address Range	Function
1F0-1F8	Fixed Disc
200-207	Games Port
210-217	Expansion Unit
220-24F	Reserved
278-27F	Parallel Port 2
2F0-2F7	Reserved
2F8-2FF	Serial Port 2
300-31F	Prototype Card
320-32F	Fixed Disc
360-36F	Reserved
378-37F	Parallel Port 1
380-38F	SDLC Bisynchronous #2
3A0-3AF	SDLC Bisynchronous #1
3B0-3BF	Monochrome Display/Printer Adapter
3C0-3CF	Reserved
3D0-3DF	Colour Graphics Adapter
3F0-3F7	Floppy Disc Controller
3F8-3FF	Serial Port 1

It might actually be possible to exploit some of the lower 512 addresses for user add-ons, but this would not be doing things in standard PC fashion, and is best avoided. It could easily lead to problems. Although the upper half of the address range is pretty crowded, there are some areas here which can be exploited for user add-ons. In particular, there are 32 addresses from &H300 to &H31F. These are reserved for prototype cards, and your own expansion cards could reasonably be deemed to be in this category. It is certainly an area of the memory map that you can use without any real risk of clashes with existing hardware. 32 addresses is not a great deal when compared to the number available on some other computers, such as the old BBC Model B computers with their two pages (512 addresses) of available address space on the expansion bus. However, this should be perfectly adequate for most users. It is sufficient for several parallel port cards, plus some analogue converter boards, or whatever.

If 32 addresses is deemed inadequate there are ways around the problem. Any addresses in the upper half of the memory map, which are not actually occupied by hardware in your computer can safely be used. This statement has to be qualified somewhat, as the real situation is that addresses of this type can be used safely by you with your particular PC system. It can not be assumed that home constructed cards that use these addresses can also be used successfully with other PCs. In practice, provided you use addresses that are reserved for an unusual piece of hardware, it is unlikely that there will be any problems. Something like the address space for the second serial port would not be a wise choice, but using the address space reserved for the SDLC Bisynchronous Port #2 would seem to be a very safe bet. There are actually a few small gaps in the input/output map which do not seem to be allocated to anything, and it would presumably be perfectly alright to exploit one or more of these.

Another means of obtaining more addresses for your add-ons is to use some of the upper address lines that are normally left unused. For instance, you could have some add-ons that use the address space from &H300 to &H31F, but which will only be activated if address line A10 is low. You could have a second piece of hardware using the same address space, but designed to operate only when A10 is high. The first set of hardware would be accessed at addresses from &H300 to &H31F, but the second set of hardware would be at addresses from &H700 to &H71F. I have never found it necessary to adopt this method, but in theory it would enable the basic range of thirty two addresses to be used many times over, giving more expansion potential than could ever be used in practice.

Finally
This covers the basics of PC interfacing in general terms. Probably the main problem for the do-it-yourself PC add-on enthusiast is that PC interfacing is a bit awkward from the mechanical point of view. However, if you use proprietary PC prototyping cards or take care to get things accurate when making your own cards, the mechanical aspects of construction should not prove to be insurmountable. In chapter 2 we will consider electronic circuits for PC address decoding, etc., and this aspect of PC interfacing is normally very straightforward. In fact interfacing to PCs is more straightforward than interfacing to many popular eight bit computers as far as the electronics is concerned. Thankfully, the PC is free from the quirky methods of interfacing used on many 8-bit computers.

Chapter 2

ISA INTERFACING

When designing ISA interface circuits the first task is to produce a suitable address decoder circuit. Although circuits of this type are generally called address decoders, in most cases they also need to decode a few lines of the control bus as well. When you access one of your add-on circuits a certain set of logic states appear on the address bus, and on certain lines of the control bus. This set of logic states should be unique to that particular add-on, and should not occur when any other circuit is being accessed. The purpose of the address decoder is to recognise this set of logic states, and to produce a change in logic level at its output while that set of logic levels persists. The output of the address decoder normally holds the data bus of the add-on circuit in an inactive state. However, when it detects the appropriate combination of input levels its change in output state activates the add-on circuit.

Bus Times
The basic way in which the add-on responds depends on whether it is a "read" or a "write" device. If the computer must read data from the circuit, once activated, the add-on's data bus will become a normal set of logic outputs. It is important to get things absolutely right with this type of circuit. If it should be activated at the wrong time, it will probably try to place data onto the data bus at the same time as some other piece of hardware. It might even try to place data onto the data bus at the same time as the microprocessor is writing data. Modern logic circuits are generally quite tolerant of this type of thing, and being realistic about it, the chances of anything being damaged are slight. On the other hand, it is clearly better not to risk any damage to expensive hardware, no matter how small the risk might be. Also, a data bus conflict of this type is almost certain to crash the computer. Continuously rebooting a crashed

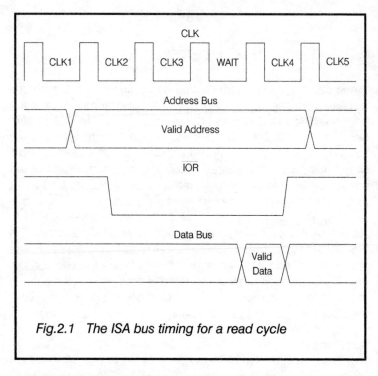

Fig.2.1 The ISA bus timing for a read cycle

computer is a good way to waste a lot of time, as many users of modern PCs will testify!

It is also important for things to be just right when writing data to an add-on circuit. The situation is slightly less critical in that when an add-on of this type is activated it reads whatever is on the data bus. If it is activated at the wrong time it will increase the loading on the data bus, but this is not likely to cause any ill effects. The data read by the device will be erroneous though, and the add-on will totally fail to function. A device that only reads from the data bus can obviously not try to force data onto the bus, and in theory at any rate, can not cause any damage or even crash the computer.

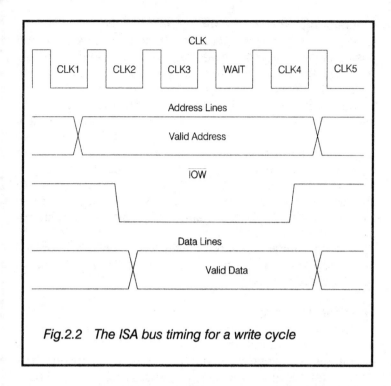

Fig.2.2 The ISA bus timing for a write cycle

Figure 2.1 shows bus timing for a read cycle. The correct address is placed on the address bus some time before valid data from the peripheral circuit must be ready and waiting on the data bus, so that it can be read by the microprocessor. Similarly, -IOR goes low well before data is present on the data bus. This gives time for the address decoder to operate and provide an active output level. The timing for a write cycle is shown in Figure 2.2. The main point to note here is that -IOW returns to the high state while valid data is still being placed onto the data bus. This causes the active output signal from the address decoder to cease, and it is this transition which is used to latch the data

In normal logic circuit terms the address decoder does not need to be particularly fast in operation. Computers, even the faster ones such as some of the more advanced PCs, are not especially fast in general electronic terms. On the other hand, the address decoder has nanoseconds rather than microseconds in which to work. Ordinary CMOS integrated circuits are not suitable as they are too slow. These components are designed for low current consumption, which is achieved at the expense of very sluggish performance. In any case, these components are not logic compatible with the PC buses. The buses of a PC operate at normal TTL levels. Ordinary 74** series devices are unsuitable as they load the buses too heavily. 74LS** series integrated circuits are well suited to this application as they are both fast and load the buses by acceptable amounts. 74HCT** components are also suitable, but the 74HC** components are not. The 74HC** logic devices operate at CMOS rather than TTL logic levels.

Practical Decoding

Here we will only be concerned with decoders for use in the prototype card address range of &H300 to &H31F. The general principles discussed here apply to interfacing using other address ranges, but obviously the address line states that have to be decoded will be different if another address range is used. As pointed out previously, it is unlikely that it would ever be necessary to use other address ranges, since the 32 available addresses from &H300 to &H31F will be sufficient for most needs. It is probably best not to attempt to use other address ranges unless you are absolutely sure you know what you are doing.

If we first consider matters in fairly broad terms, the minimal address decoding needed is to decode address lines A5 to A9. Additionally, AEN must be decoded, together with -IOR and (or) -IOW. These are the states of these lines when an input address in the range &H300 to &H31F is accessed.

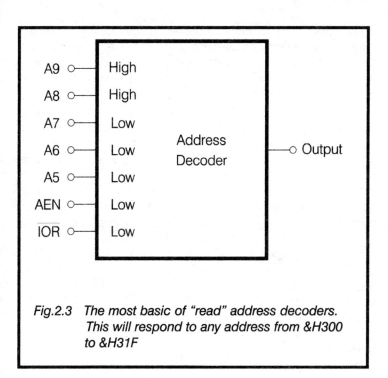

Fig.2.3   The most basic of "read" address decoders. This will respond to any address from &H300 to &H31F

Line	Logic State
A5	Low
A6	Low
A7	Low
A8	High
A9	High
AEN	Low
-IOR	Low
-IOW	High

For read operations the state of -IOW is irrelevant, and it does not need to be decoded. This gives us the basic read address decoder represented diagrammatically in Figure 2.3. This will respond to any read operation to an input device in the address range &H300 to &H31F, but it should ignore any other read operations, as well as all write types and memory accesses. Most decoders are designed to have an output that is normally high and which goes low when the circuit is activated. Not all peripheral circuits require things this way round though, and where appropriate the decoder must be designed to have an output that is normally low, and which pulses high while it is activated. Remember that in order to convert a decoder from one type to the other you merely need to add an inverter at the output.

This is the set of states that must be decoded when an output circuit in the relevant address range is accessed.

Line	Logic State
A5	Low
A6	Low
A7	Low
A8	High
A9	High
AEN	Low
-IOR	High
-IOW	Low

This is the same as before, but the states of -IOR and -IOW have been reversed. In this case it is -IOR that can be ignored and -IOW that must be decoded. This basic "write" decoder is shown diagrammatically in Figure 2.4. When designing any address decoder or similar logic circuits it is a good idea to write down the decoded state of each line, or produce a diagram of the type shown in Figure 2.4, so that you get a clear picture of what is required. This can help to avoid time consuming errors.

In practice you will not always need an address decoder specifically for a read circuit or a write type. Most practical interfacing applications involve both reading and writing to the peripheral circuit. Even if the purpose of a port is (say) to output

40

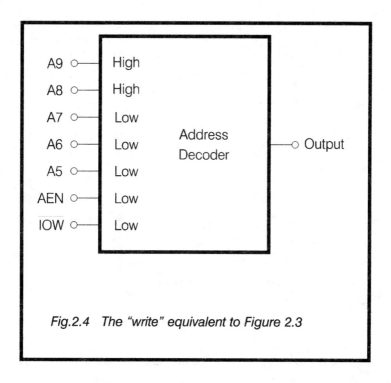

Fig.2.4 The "write" equivalent to Figure 2.3

eight-bit bytes of data, it may well consist of more than just eight output lines. It is often necessary to carefully control the flow of data from the basic eight-bit port to some further hardware. This requires one or more handshake lines, one of which will probably be an input to monitor the status of the secondary piece of hardware. A Centronics type parallel printer port is a good example of an eight-bit output port of this type. It includes a strobe output that provides a pulse each time a fresh byte of data is placed on the data outputs. It has two handshake inputs ("Acknowledge" and "Busy"), one of which is used to indicate whether or not the printer is ready to receive further data. The correct flow of data into or out of the computer is something you need to consider carefully when undertaking do-it-yourself interfacing. Get this aspect of things slightly wrong,

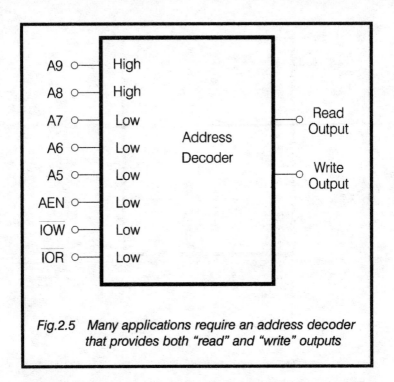

Fig.2.5   Many applications require an address decoder that provides both "read" and "write" outputs

and you may well find yourself having to do a complete redesign and rebuilding job on the add-on card.

One way of tackling the problem of combined read and write address decoding is to produce two separate address decoders, one for each function. This has to be regarded as doing things the hard way, and is also not a strictly valid method of PC interfacing. Each line of the PC expansion bus should be loaded by no more than one 74LS** series TTL input, or an equivalent amount. Using two address decoders would load some lines with two inputs. In practice this would probably not matter too much, and there are ways around the problem. One of these is to add buffers on the relevant lines so that these limit the loading

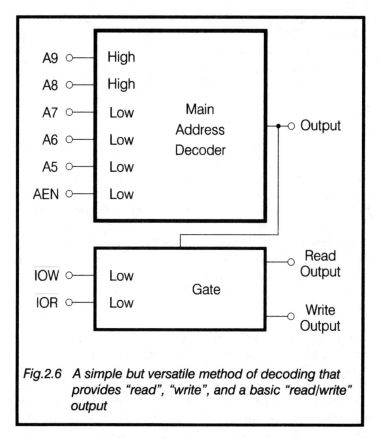

Fig.2.6 *A simple but versatile method of decoding that provides "read", "write", and a basic "read/write" output*

of the bus lines to one 74LS** TTL load. This further adds to the complication and expense of the address decoder though.

In general it is better to produce an all-in-one address decoder of the type depicted in Figure 2.5. With AEN and the five address inputs at the appropriate states, the "Read" output is activated if -IOR is low, and the "Write" output is activated if -IOW is low. While it is quite possible to produce a decoder of this type, in practice it is often easier to have a decoder that does not process -IOR or -IOW. The output of this simple decoder is then fed to a further decoder, which does process -IOW and -IOR. This scheme of things is shown in Figure 2.6. The gate circuit, which generates the separate "Read" and "Write" outputs, can be very simple indeed. This system is very versatile in that it also provides a combined "read/write" output, which is what is needed for some peripheral chips. This type of decoder is therefore apposite to just about any method of interfacing.

The interface chips that require a combined "read/write" decoder output are the 82** series which are specifically designed for operation with 8080 series microprocessors. There are actually a number of other peripheral chips that are designed to be bus compatible with the 8080 series of microprocessors. These are less common than the 82** series chips, but you may well encounter some devices of this type. These chips are all used in the manner shown in Figure 2.7. The address decoder only has to process AEN plus address lines A5 to A9. -IOR and -IOW are not simply ignored, but are instead decoded by the appropriate inputs of the 82** series integrated circuit.

So far we have only considered the situation where a single input register and one output register are to be used. The address decoder has treated the &H300 to &H31F address range as if it was a single address. The peripheral circuit effectively occupies all these addresses, and can be operated using any address in this range. This means that no other devices can exist in this address range, which is obviously a bit restrictive. With many of the 82** series chips there are several registers, and each chip must therefore occupy several addresses, with a different register located at each address.

This is easily accomplished, as the 82** series integrated circuits have more than one read/write register, but also have one or more register select inputs. These extras are simply fed from the address bus, and would normally be fed from the least significant address lines (i.e. A0, A1, etc.). In the example set-

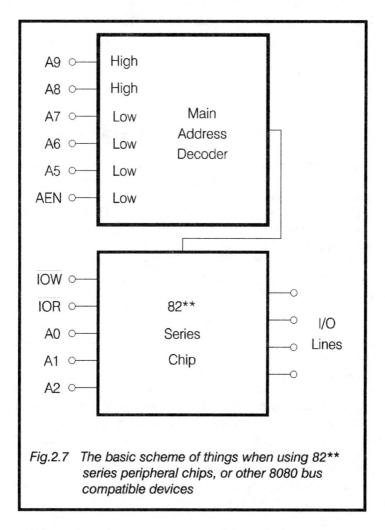

Fig.2.7 *The basic scheme of things when using 82***
        series peripheral chips, or other 8080 bus
        compatible devices

up of Figure 2.7 there are three register select inputs which are
fed from address lines A0 to A2. This table shows the number
of registers available for various numbers of chip select inputs.

No. Of C/S Inputs	Maximum No. Of Registers
0	1
1	2
2	4
3	8
4	16

In the example of Figure 2.7 there are three chip select inputs fed from three address lines. This gives a maximum of eight read registers and eight write types. These registers are at addresses from &H300 to &H308. However, as less than full address decoding is being used, with A3 and A4 being left unprocessed, the full range of thirty-two addresses remain occupied. The eight registers appear again as an echo at addresses &H309 to &H30F. There are further echoes at &H310 to &H318, and &H319 to &H31F. This blocks any further add-ons being used in the &H300 to &H31F address range.

Two 82** series peripheral chips can be used in a set-up of the type shown in Figure 2.8. The two chips are connected to the expansion bus in parallel. We are ignoring the data bus in these address-decoding examples, but this is simply connected to the data bus of the expansion port. The address decoder has two outputs, one for each peripheral chip. These outputs cover different address ranges. In practice this can only be achieved by processing further address lines.

Conventionally, it would be address line A4 that was decoded. One peripheral would be activated when A4 was high, the other would be activated when it was low. This would put the first peripheral device (A4 low) at addresses from &H300 to &H308, and at echoes from &H309 to &H30F. The second peripheral (A4 high) would be at addresses from &H310 to &H318, and at echoes from &H319 to &H31F. By also decoding A3 it would be possible to have four chips. The two extra chips would occupy the address ranges that were previously occupied by echoes. More than four chips having eight registers would not be

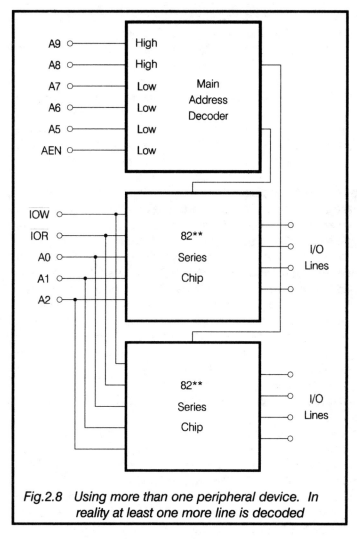

Fig.2.8   Using more than one peripheral device. In reality at least one more line is decoded

possible, as this would require more than the available 32 addresses. As pointed out previously, there are ways of obtaining greater expansion, but it is unlikely that more than 32 read registers and 32 write types would be needed.

One slight flaw with this method of using devices in parallel is that some lines of the expansion bus are loaded by more than one input. In particular, the data bus will be loaded by several inputs. This does not necessarily matter in practice, since there should only be one input in the active state at any one time. The loading is therefore much less than it might at first appear. However, in this sort of situation you can always play safe by including buffers on the lines which might otherwise be excessively loaded.

Gates and Decoders

There is no single solution to address decoding problems, and there are often dozens of different ways of achieving much the same thing. Some solutions are more practical than others. In general, it is better to use simple gates and inverters. These are fast in operation and inexpensive. They do sometimes have a disadvantage, which is that it can take a lot of inter-wiring in order to get a few gates and inverters to give the desired action. For a home constructed unit it may sometimes be better to opt for more complex devices, such as three to eight line decoders, in order to keep the board layout reasonably simple and straightforward.

The more complex decoder integrated circuits can be quite expensive, and are often relatively slow in operation. These may actually be perfectly usable for PC address decoding, but it should be possible to find good ways of handling the decoding without resorting to any of the more exotic 74LS** series of integrated circuits. The two basic types of logic gate are the AND and OR varieties. Logic gates all have two or more inputs, and a single output. If we consider a simple two input AND gate first, the truth table provided below shows the function it performs.

INPUT 1	INPUT 2	OUTPUT
Low	Low	Low
Low	High	Low
High	Low	Low
High	High	High

Its output is low unless input 1 AND input 2 are high, and it is from this that the AND name is derived. The action is much the same if there are more inputs. With all the inputs high, the output is high. If one or more of the inputs are low, the output is low.

This is the truth table for a 2 input OR gate.

INPUT 1	INPUT 2	OUTPUT
Low	Low	Low
Low	High	High
High	Low	High
High	High	High

The output of a two input OR gate is low unless one OR other of its inputs is high, and it is from this that the OR name is derived. Again, the action of the gate remains much the same if there are more than two inputs. With none of the inputs in the high state the output will be low, but if one or more of the inputs should go high, the output will also go high.

There are couple of variations on the AND and OR gates, and these are called NAND and NOR gates. These are the truth tables for two input NAND and NOR gates respectively.

INPUT 1	INPUT 2	OUTPUT
Low	Low	High
Low	High	High
High	Low	High
High	High	Low

INPUT 1	INPUT 2	OUTPUT
Low	Low	High
Low	High	Low
High	Low	Low
High	High	Low

These really only differ from the original truth tables in that the output states are reversed. In effect, a NAND gate is an AND gate with its output fed through an inverter. Therefore, if input 1 and input 2 are taken high, the output goes low. Any other set of input states sends the output high. Similarly, a NOR gate is effectively just an OR gate with its output inverted.

There is actually a fifth type of gate, but this is little used in practice. It is the exclusive OR (XOR) gate, which is similar to an OR gate. However, with an OR gate, the output is not simply high if input 1 or input 2 is high. If both inputs are taken to the high state, then the output will still go high. With an exclusive OR gate taking just one input high will send the output high. Having no inputs set high, or more than one input set to the high state, results in the output going low. I suppose that this could reasonably be regarded as the true OR gate action, but in practice it tends to be less useful that the conventional OR gate action, and exclusive OR gates are something of a rarity. There are also exclusive NOR gates and these are effectively just an exclusive OR gate with an inverter at the output.

Figure 2.9 shows the circuit symbols for the various types of two input gate. It also shows the circuit symbols for an inverter and a multi-input (NAND) gate. Note that gate circuit symbols seem to be less rigidly standardised than most other circuit symbols, and that you may well encounter different gate symbols in other publications. However, it is usually fairly obvious what type of gate each symbol is meant to depict.

Of the various decoder chips available the 74LS138 is probably the most useful low cost type for address decoding

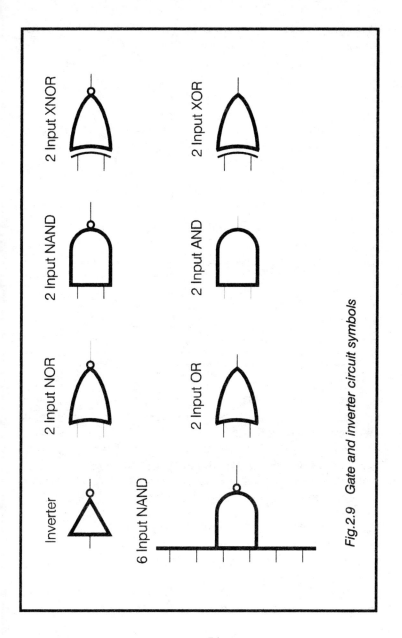

Fig.2.9   Gate and inverter circuit symbols

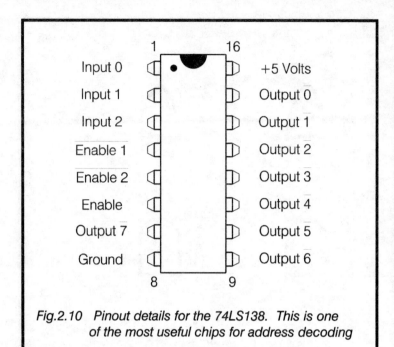

Fig.2.10 Pinout details for the 74LS138. This is one of the most useful chips for address decoding

purposes. Pinout details for this 16 pin DIL chip are shown in Figure 2.10. It is a three to eight line decoder, and it has outputs that are normally high. One of the outputs goes to the low state, and which output this is depends on the binary pattern fed to the three inputs. For those who are not familiar with the binary numbering system, this table shows which set of input states activates each output.

INPUT 0	INPUT 1	INPUT 2	OUTPUT
Low	Low	Low	0
Low	Low	High	1
Low	High	Low	2
Low	High	High	3
High	Low	Low	4

High	Low	High	5
High	High	Low	6
High	High	High	7

The 74LS138 is rather more useful than it might at first appear. The first point to note is that there are three further inputs. In most cases it is not limited to decoding three lines, and can actually decode up to six lines. The additional three lines are "enable" types, and unless they are taken to the appropriate state, the outputs of the device all go to the third logic state. In other words they simply go to a high impedance state, and will not drive logic inputs. The inputs at pins 4 and 5 are negative enable inputs, and they must be taken to logic 0 in order to make the device function normally. The enable input at pin 6 is a positive type, and this pin must be taken high in order to produce normal operation of the chip.

The second point to note is that different sets of input states activate different outputs of the 74LS138. This gives the potential of having the device decode several blocks of addresses, with each block having its own output. Even if you do not require several decoded outputs on one card, it is possible to standardise on the same decoder circuit for several cards, with a different output being used on each card. You could, for example, have the &H300 to &H31F address range split into four blocks of eight addresses, with each block activating a different output of the 74LS138. You could then have up to four do-it-yourself expansion cards using the same basic address decoder circuit, provided each card utilized a different output of its address decoder.

Decoder Circuits
A popular method of PC address decoding is to have a decoder circuit based on a 74LS30 eight input NAND gate. This has an output that goes low if all eight inputs are high, or high if any of the inputs are low. Obviously you will not need a PC address decoder that decodes eight lines to the high state. Typically the

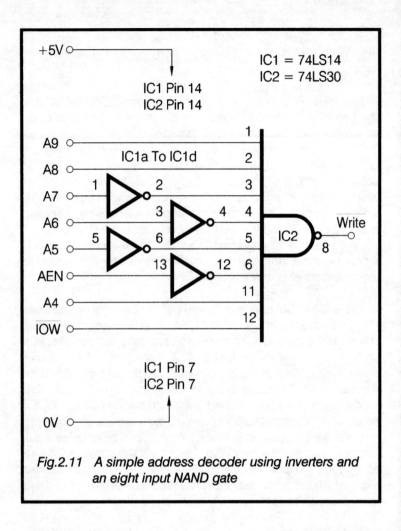

Fig.2.11 A simple address decoder using inverters and an eight input NAND gate

requirement is for something more like a decoder which is activated by four lines high and four lines low. The simple way around this problem is to feed to the 74LS30 via inverters any lines that must be decoded to the low state.

Figure 2.11 shows a typical address decoder based on a 74LS30 eight input NAND gate plus some inverters. In this case there are four inverters, and these are part of a 74LS14 hex Schmitt trigger/inverter package. However, this general scheme of things should work properly using any 74LS** series inverters. This decoder is designed to act as a "Write" decoder. It decodes A4, A8, and A9 to the high state and A5 to A7 to the low state. This means that it will be activated when any address from &H310 to &H31F is accessed for a write operation. If A4 was to be fed to IC2 via an inverter, it would then be decoded to the low state, and the circuit would be activated by write operations to addresses from &H300 to &H30F. Connect -IOR instead of -IOW, and the decoder will then act as a read type.

This type of address decoder is very cheap and simple, but as pointed out previously, it can be a bit awkward when it comes to actually building the circuit. It is also slightly lacking in versatility. Figure 2.12 shows the circuit diagram for a PC address decoder based on a 74LS138. This is still pretty cheap and simple, but it is much more versatile than the circuit based on the 74LS30.

A minimalist PC address decoder would have to decode address lines from A5 to A9, plus AEN and possibly -IOR or -IOW. It is just possible to do this using a 74LS138, with the only proviso that any decoding of -IOR or -IOW must be provided separately. Figure 2.13 shows the circuit for a minimalist address decoder of this type, and I suppose this could be used if you only wanted to have (say) one 8255 parallel interface chip in the &H300 to &H31F address space. However, by using a very simple address decoder of this type you would be painting yourself into the proverbial corner, and it would be difficult to add more user add-ons at a later date.

The circuit of Figure 2.12 offers much greater versatility, but it requires the use of an extra chip. This is a 74LS27 triple three input NOR gate. In this circuit only two of the gates are required,

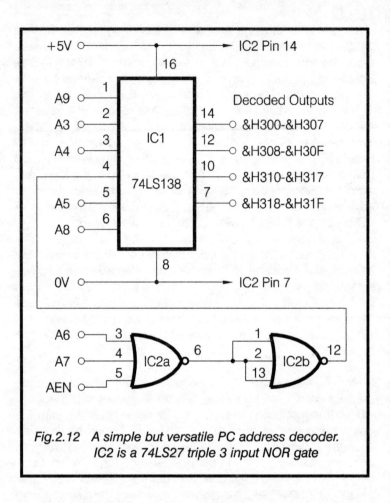

Fig.2.12 A simple but versatile PC address decoder.
IC2 is a 74LS27 triple 3 input NOR gate

and no connections are made to the third gate. IC2b is simply wired as an inverter, and it effectively converts IC2a into a three input OR gate. It might seem to be easier to simply use a three input OR gate, but a suitable device seems to be difficult to obtain. The 74LS27 is widely available, and is easily wired to give the required circuit action.

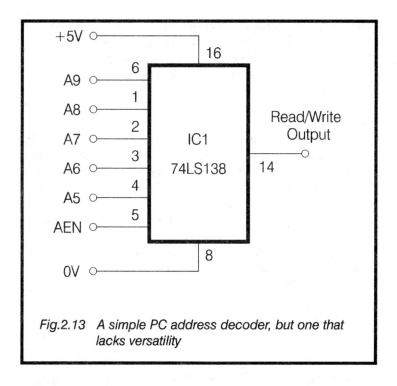

Fig.2.13 A simple PC address decoder, but one that
lacks versatility

This arrangement enables three lines to drive one input of
the 74LS138, permitting a maximum of eight rather than six lines
to be decoded. A6, A7, and AEN are decoded to the low state
by the gates and one of the low enable inputs of IC1. The other
low enable input decodes A5, while the high enable input
decodes A8. A9 is fed to input 0, and it is effectively decoded to
the high state. This renders four of IC1's eight outputs effectively
inoperative. Inputs 1 and 2 of IC1 decode A3 and A4, and the
states on these lines, when all the other decoded lines are at
the appropriate logic levels, dictate which of the four outputs of
IC1 is activated. In other words, the &H300 to &H31F address
range is divided into four blocks of eight addresses. Figure
2.12 shows the range of addresses that activates each output.

If you only wanted two blocks of sixteen addresses, then A3 would not be decoded, and instead, pin 2 of IC1 would be connected to the 0-volt supply rail. The output at pin 14 would then be activated by addresses from &H300 to &H30F, and the output at pin 10 would be activated by addresses from &H310 to &H31F. Obviously more address decoding can be added if more but smaller blocks of addresses are needed. This can be accomplished using another gate or gates ahead of one or more of IC1's inputs. This would enable A9 to be decoded elsewhere, leaving input 0 (pin 1) of IC1 free to decode A2. All eight outputs of IC1 would then be brought into action. However, for most purposes the address decoder of Figure 2.12 will suffice without resorting to any modifications. Blocks of eight addresses are sufficient to accommodate most add-ons, while four blocks should give enough scope for expansion. With one address block per add-on card, this would be sufficient to use up all the expansion slots in most computers.

As already pointed out, with some peripheral chips there is no need to bother about decoding -IOW and -IOR, since some chips provide inputs for these lines and do the necessary decoding. This is not always the case though, and when using circuits that are wholly or largely based on TTL logic chips, you will normally have to decode -IOR and -IOW. Figure 2.14 shows a simple PC address decoder and the additional circuitry needed in order to produce separate read and write output signals. This basically just consists of processing the -IOW line and the output of the decoder using a two input OR gate. During a write operation to the appropriate address range, both of these lines will go low, and so will the output of the gate. Essentially the same system is used with a second OR gate to process the -IOR line and produce a read output. A negative chip select output is still available from the basic address decoder circuit, and can be used with any chips that have built-in processing for -IOW and -IOR. Note that this method of gating should work perfectly well with any address decoder circuit, but only if it provides negative output pulses.

Parallel I/O Ports

In order to produce an eight bit output port all that is needed is an address decoder plus an eight bit latch. Simply using something like a tristate eight-bit buffer to provide an output port is not usually acceptable. This would only provide a valid output for the duration that the data bus was fed through to the outputs. This is likely to be well under a microsecond in practice. What is needed is a circuit that will latch this momentary flash of data, so that the outputs can be used to drive relays, l.e.d.s, digital to analogue converters, or whatever. The situation is generally somewhat different when it comes to inputting data. You normally have a set of what are essentially static input levels, and these must be fed through to the data bus while the port is read. An eight-bit tristate buffer is all that is needed to achieve this.

Figure 2.15 shows the circuit diagram for a basic PC eight-bit input/output port. This is basically the same sort of circuit that has been used with numerous eight-bit home computers over the years, and it seems to work reliably with most PCs. Note that this circuit must be used in conjunction with a suitable address decoder circuit. This must be a decoder that includes the extra decoding to provide separate read and write outputs.

It is also worth noting that although no supply decoupling capacitors are featured in any of the circuits in this book, these must be included on any PC expansion cards. These are merely ceramic capacitors of about 100 nanofarads in value connected across the supply lines. Some circuit designers use one capacitor per TTL integrated circuit, with each capacitor mounted as close as possible to its respective integrated circuit. However, this is probably using a certain amount of over-kill, and one decoupling capacitor per three TTL integrated circuits (or other logic chips) should suffice.

The eight-bit output port of Figure 2.15 is provided by a 74LS273 octal D type flip/flop. The data bus connects to its D

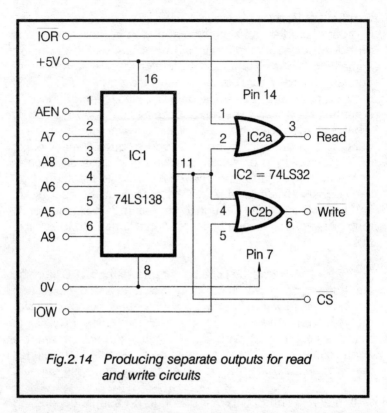

Fig.2.14 Producing separate outputs for read and write circuits

(data) inputs, and the latching output lines are provided by the Q outputs. These are non-inverting outputs which latch at whatever states are present on the D inputs when there is a positive transition on the CP (clock pulse) input. This transition is, of course, provided by the trailing edge of the write pulse from the address decoder.

The input port is provided by a 74LS245 octal transceiver (IC4). Conventionally an octal tristate buffer such as a 74LS244 is used in applications of this type. I prefer to use the 74LS245 simply because its pinout arrangement is a more convenient one which helps to keep board layouts more simple and

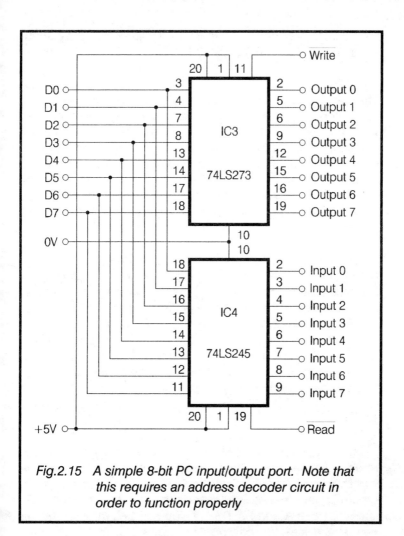

*Fig.2.15   A simple 8-bit PC input/output port. Note that
this requires an address decoder circuit in
order to function properly*

straightforward. In this case IC4 has pin 1 wired to the +5 volt
supply so that it is permanently in the "send" mode. Its tristate
outputs are controlled by the negative chip enable input at pin
19. When a negative pulse is received from the read output of

the address decoder, the outputs are activated and the eight bit input code is fed through to the PC's data bus.

The 8255

The standard parallel interface chip for the PCs (and many other computers come to that) is the 8255. This is bus compatible with the 8080 and 8086 series of microprocessors, and with the Z80 series. The Z80A microprocessor has been used in several popular eight-bit home computers, and the 8255 was popular in user add-ons for these machines. This chip may well be familiar to many readers, but it will be described in reasonable detail for the benefit of those who have not encountered it previously.

It is a 40-pin DIL chip, which provides three eight bit input/output ports. This is one eight-bit port more than many parallel interface adapter chips, such as the 6522 and 6821. However, it is not quite as good as it may at first appear. Whereas chips such as the 6522 only provide two eight bit ports, they also provide two handshake lines per port. These handshake lines are sufficiently versatile to accommodate any normal handshaking arrangements. This enables the two eight bit ports to operate properly in any normal situations, including those where controlling the flow of data into or out of the port is critical and difficult.

By contrast, the ports of the 8255 have no handshake lines at all. Instead, where handshaking is needed, port C is split into two four bit ports. One nibble is set as outputs while the other nibble is set as inputs, and these act as the handshake lines for Ports A and B. Thus, if you need eight bit ports plus handshake lines, you only have two ports, plus (probably) a few leftover input and output lines from port C. If you require just basic input or output ports with no handshaking, then the 8255 has more to offer than most other parallel interface adapters. On the other hand, if you do require handshaking it is little advantage. Although it might provide a few spare lines on port C, it is probably slightly less convenient to use than most other parallel port chips.

It is only fair to point out another relative shortcoming of the 8255, which is a lack of individual control over the functions of its input/output lines. With devices such as the 6522 and 6821 there is a data direction register for each port. By way of this register it is possible to set each line as an input or an output, as desired. If you require a port to have five lines as outputs to control relay drivers, and three as inputs to read sensor switches, then this is perfectly possible. You have full control over which lines are used as the inputs and which are set as the outputs. With the 8255 all eight lines of a port must be set as outputs, or all eight must be set as inputs. The only exception to this is port C. As explained previously, this can be set for simple split operation (four lines as inputs and four lines as outputs).

Figure 2.16 gives pinout details for the 8255, and it also shows the correct method of connecting it to the PC expansion bus. The negative chip select input (pin 6) is fed from the address decoder, which must obviously be a type that provides negative output pulses (as do the address decoder circuits featured earlier in this chapter). The RST, -IOW, and -IOR lines of the control bus all connect to corresponding terminals of the 8255, as does the 8 bit data bus. There are two register select inputs on the 8255, which would normally connect to A0 and A1. Accordingly, they are called A0 and A1 rather than RS0 and RS1 (or something similar). If the address decoder responds (say) to eight addresses from &H308 to &H30F, then the 8255 will occupy four addresses from &H308 to &H30B. It will also occupy addresses from &H30C to &H30F in the form of one set of echoes. Therefore, these addresses would be unusable for other purposes. Of course, the 8255 could be placed in just four addresses with no echoes, but in most cases there will not be a great enough shortage of address space to make this worthwhile.

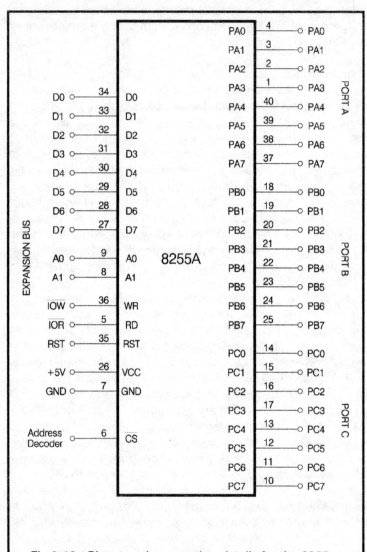

Fig.2.16 Pinout and connection details for the 8255

The outputs of the 8255 are latching types, and are compatible with 74LS** and 74HCT** TTL devices. The inputs are also compatible with these devices. In fact the device will work reliably with most logic devices, including most CMOS types.

Although it might seem better to use simple TTL input and output ports for most applications, the 8255 tends to be a more popular choice. One reason for this is undoubtedly that it provides a reasonably simple and inexpensive means of providing a lot of input/output lines. Also, it is designed specifically for operation with microprocessors such as the 8088 and 80286, etc., and should operate very reliably with these. I have encountered one or two PCs that seem to be something less than 100% reliable when used with some simple TTL output ports, especially when operating at higher bus speeds. I have never experienced any problems when using the 8255 though, regardless of the bus speed. I therefore tend to use it as my standard method of interfacing the PC expansion bus to digital to analogue converters, speech chips, or whatever.

8255 Programming
There is insufficient space available here to go into great detail about all the 8255 operating modes, and methods of using this device. Anyone using practically any computer peripheral chip would be well advised to obtain the relevant data sheet, and I would certainly recommend this for anyone who is going to use a chip as complex as the 8255. However, here we will consider the basic ways of using this interface chip, which should at least get you started, and may be all that you need in order to use the chip effectively in your particular applications.

The 8255 has four read/write registers. Three of these are ports A, B, and C. Obviously each one of these would normally be used only as a read register or a write type, depending on whether its port has been set as an input or an output type. The exception to this is when port C is used in the split mode of operation, and it is then a form of read/write register. The fourth

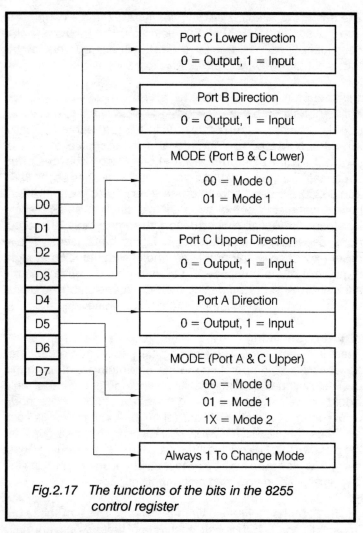

Port C Lower Direction
0 = Output, 1 = Input

Port B Direction
0 = Output, 1 = Input

MODE (Port B & C Lower)
00 = Mode 0 01 = Mode 1

Port C Upper Direction
0 = Output, 1 = Input

Port A Direction
0 = Output, 1 = Input

MODE (Port A & C Upper)
00 = Mode 0 01 = Mode 1 1X = Mode 2

Always 1 To Change Mode

D0
D1
D2
D3
D4
D5
D6
D7

*Fig.2.17   The functions of the bits in the 8255
control register*

register is a control type, and data would normally only be written to this. You can read data from this register, but it will not furnish anything meaningful. If you need a record of what has been written to the control register, a byte of RAM must be used to store a copy of each control number that is written to this register. If we assume that the 8255 is at the example address range mentioned earlier (&H308 to &H30B), then the base addresses of the four registers would be as follows:

HEX ADDRESS	DEC. ADDRESS	REGISTER
&H308	776	Port A
&H309	777	Port B
&H30A	778	Port C
&H30B	779	Control

Using the ports is straightforward enough, but the control register is a bit tricky to fully master. There are three modes of operation for the 8255, which have been designated modes 0, 1, and 2. Mode 0 is the most simple, and is the one you should use when initially experimenting with the 8255. In this mode the ports operate as simple input/output types, with the only complication that port C can operate in the split mode (one nibble as inputs and the other nibble as outputs).

Bits five to seven of the control register set the required operating mode. Bit seven is set high in order to enable the operating mode to be changed. Be careful to set this bit high, as the control register operates in a totally different manner if this bit is set to zero. Bits five and six control the operating mode. This table shows how this scheme of things operates.

MODE	BIT 7	BIT 6	BIT 5
0	1	0	0
1	1	0	1
2	1	1	0
2	1	1	1

As will be apparent from this table, there are two control codes which select mode 2. It does not matter which one you use, the effect on the 8255 is exactly the same. These bits only control the mode of port A and the upper nibble of port C. Port B and the lower nibble of port C are controlled by bit 2 of the control register. This is either high for mode 1 operation, or low if you require mode 0 operation. Mode 2 is not applicable to these ports, and so one bit is all that is needed for their mode control.

Bits zero, one, three, and four are used to control the functions of the ports (i.e. whether they operate as inputs or outputs). This operates in the following manner.

PORT	CONTROL BIT	DEC. VALUE WHEN HIGH
0	C Lower	1
1	B	2
3	C Upper	8
4	A	16

In order to set a port as an output type the control bit is set to zero. Setting a control bit to 1 obviously sets its respective port as an input type. Those who are used to the 6522, 6821, etc., should note that this works the opposite way round to the data direction registers of these chips.

When writing to the control register you must set the mode of operation and the port directions in a single write operation. You can not write to bits five to seven first and then bits zero, one, three, and four. However, working out the right control register values is not difficult. For mode 0 operation bits five and six are low, and bit seven is high. To set bit seven high a decimal value of 128 is required. The table provided previously shows the decimal value needed for each control bit when it is set high (i.e. when its port is to be set as an input). A value of zero is, of course, needed for any bits that will be set low.

Simply take the values given in the table for the ports that are to be set as inputs, and add 128 to the total of these values. You then have the value to write to the control register. For Example, assume that port A and both nibbles of port C are to be set as inputs. The values for these ports as inputs are sixteen, eight, and one. This gives a total of 25. Adding 128 to this gives a grand total of 153, which is the value that must be written to the control register. In GW BASIC, and using the example port addresses mentioned previously, this value would be written to the control register using the instruction:

OUT 779,153

You can use hexadecimal addresses with GW BASIC if you prefer, but remember that hexadecimal numbers are indicated using the "&H" prefix, not just the "&" prefix used in some languages. Numbers having just the "&" prefix may well be accepted, as I think that these are interpreted by GW BASIC as octal (base eight) numbers. This has led me into some time consuming errors in the past as I tend to use just the "&" prefix from force of habit (having mainly used a BBC computers for interfacing in the past). Consequently, I now always use decimal input/output addresses when using GW BASIC.

For many purposes mode 0 operation will suffice. For example, there are many applications that do not require any form of handshaking. These include such things as driving digital to analogue converters, relay drivers, etc., and reading simple sensors. For applications of this type you only need simple input and output lines, and there is no point in using anything beyond mode 0. Where handshaking is needed, setting port C for split operation to provide the handshake input/output lines will often suffice. This does not provide edge-triggered inputs or anything of this type, but simple input and output lines will usually be sufficient. Remember that where necessary you can always use some external signal processing, such as a pulse stretcher or shortener, in order to make things more reliable. For instance, if an output is providing very brief pulses, a pulse stretcher might provide a signal, which can be read more reliably, with no pulses passing undetected by the handshake input.

Where complex handshaking is needed it might be better to resort to mode 1 operation. This uses port A and port B as eight bit input output ports, and six lines of port C to act as strobed handshake lines and interrupt control signals (three lines per port). Mode 2 provides strobed bidirectional operation through port A, with five lines of port C acting, as what I suppose is a sort of control bus. This is not a mode that I have ever used, and it is presumably only needed for a few specialised applications. Anyway, to fully get to grips with the 8255 you really need to study the data sheet and then experiment a little.

Other 82** series devices interface to the PC buses in much the same way as the 8255. Devices that are bus compatible with the 82** series of peripheral chips should also interface to the PC expansion bus without difficulty. It is often possible to interface peripheral chips for one series of microprocessors to a microprocessor from a different range. For example, chips intended for the 6502 and similar microprocessors have been used successfully with the Z80 microprocessor. It is usually possible to overcome the differences between the control buses, but it can take a certain amount of experimentation to get things right. For example, where a peripheral chip has a combined read/write line, either -IOW or -IOR might provide a suitable signal. If not, then inverting one of these lines or feeding it through a monostable might produce the desired result. If a negative reset signal is needed, then feeding the PC's reset line via an inverter should give the desired result, or you can put a suitable reset generator circuit on the expansion card. Studying the timing diagrams in data sheets can steer you in the right direction, but in the end it comes down to the "suck it and see" approach.

Design Example
Bear in mind that devices which are described as "microprocessor bus compatible", or something similar, might not be compatible with the PCs version of a microprocessor bus. While most microprocessor compatible devices can

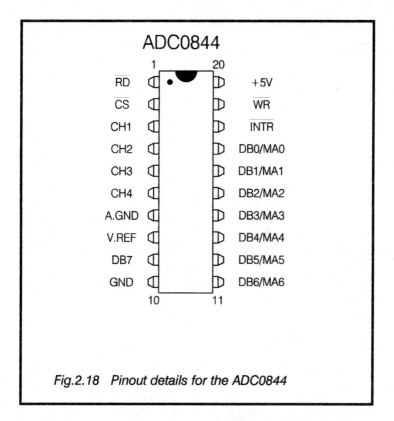

ADC0844

$\overline{RD}$	1	20	+5V
$\overline{CS}$			$\overline{WR}$
CH1			$\overline{INTR}$
CH2			DB0/MA0
CH3			DB1/MA1
CH4			DB2/MA2
A.GND			DB3/MA3
V.REF			DB4/MA4
DB7			DB5/MA5
GND	10	11	DB6/MA6

Fig.2.18   Pinout details for the ADC0844

probably be interfaced direct to the PC buses successfully, this may not always be feasible. With some peripheral chips it is probably best not to attempt to interface them direct onto the PC expansion bus. You have to carefully assess each interfacing problem, and work out the most appropriate solution. When in doubt it is probably best to take the safer but more complex approach, and interface to the PC expansion bus indirectly via an 8255 (or whatever).

We will now consider an example of interfacing devices to the PC bus, in order to illustrate the problems that can arise and some possible solutions to them. We will use an analogue to digital as our design example as this is fairly typical in the interfacing problems it provides. The circuits described here can actually be used as the basis of your own projects, as we will be dealing with practical integrated circuits, not notional devices. The circuits have all been tried and tested.

Some devices are much easier to interface to the PC expansion bus than others, and the ADC0844 analogue to digital converter represents a relatively easy option. Pinout details for this device are shown in Figure 2.18. The ADC0844 is relatively easy to interface to a PC because it is specifically designed to interface to 8080 and 8088 type buses. This analogue to digital converter chip has an eight-bit data bus (DB0 to DB7) with tristate outputs. It can therefore output to the data bus by driving the chip select (-CS) input from a suitable address decoder circuit. There is no need for the address decoder to process -IOR or -IOW as there are inputs for these on the ADC0844 (-RD and -WR).

You will notice from Figure 2.18 that the lower four bits of the address bus are labelled DB0/MA0 to DB3/MA3. This is due to the fact that these pins are dual purpose, and also operate as what the ADC0844 data sheet refers to as address inputs. This is perhaps not a strictly accurate way of looking at things since the chip only occupies a single address, and these pins do slightly more than switch between several internal registers. The basic method of using the ADC0844 is to first write to the device in order to start a conversion, and to then read it in order to extract the converted value. Sometimes with this type of thing the value written to the chip is simply a dummy value, and can be any legal value (i.e. any integer from 0 to 255). The ADC0844 is a fairly complex device though, and it has four analogue inputs. There is actually only one converter, but this is preceded by a four way multiplexer (an electronic switch) that can connect any one of these inputs through to the converter. The value written to the device determines which input is connected through to the converter.

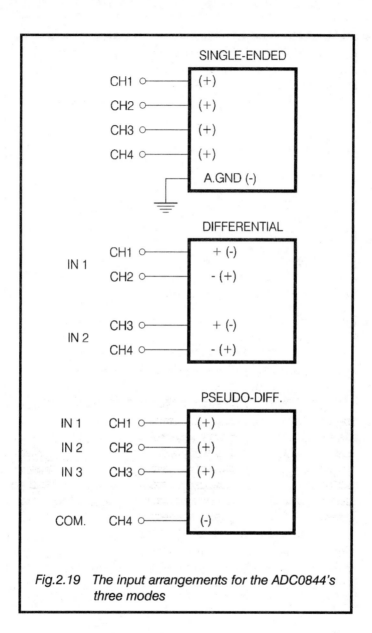

Fig.2.19   The input arrangements for the ADC0844's three modes

73

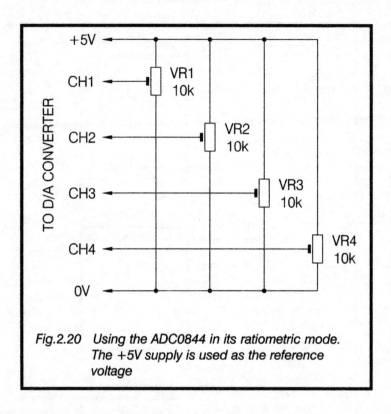

*Fig.2.20   Using the ADC0844 in its ratiometric mode.
The +5V supply is used as the reference
voltage*

Matters are actually a bit more complicated than this, because there are three modes of operation available. The most simple of these is the single-ended mode, and with this there are four inputs. The voltage converted is the potential from the analogue ground pin to whichever input has been selected. In other words, this is the normal four-channel mode of the device. You will notice from Figure 2.18 that there are separate analogue and digital ground terminals. These do not necessarily have to be held at the same potential, but in most cases they would simply be wired together and connected to a common analogue/digital ground.

74

There are two differential modes available, and in the standard differential mode there are two inputs available. The first uses what would normally be the channel 1 and channel 2 inputs, while the second uses the channel 3 and channel 4 inputs. The other differential mode is a pseudo type, in which the channel 4 input acts as a common negative input, and the other three inputs respond to their voltage relative to the channel 4 input. In other words, if you wish to measure voltages with respect to a potential other than the earth one, connect the channel 4 input to a suitable offset voltage, and then use inputs 1 to 3 to measure the voltages. Note that in the differential and pseudo differential modes the analogue ground terminal is not used as an input, but it would normally be connected to ground anyway. Figure 2.19 shows the available modes in diagrammatic form, and might help to clarify matters.

This table shows the values that must be written to the ADC0844 in order to select each of the available operating modes, and the options available within each mode (e.g. which channel is to be read). The table shows the polarity with which the input signals must be applied to the device.

CTRL VAL	CH1	CH2	CH3	CH4	A.GND	MODE
0	+	-	X	X	X	Differential
1	-	+	X	X	X	Differential
2	X	X	+	-	X	Differential
3	X	X	-	+	X	Differential
4	+	X	X	X	-	Single-ended
5	X	+	X	X	-	Single-ended
6	X	X	+	X	-	Single-ended
7	X	X	X	+	-	Single-ended
12	+	X	X	-	X	Pseudo Diff.
13	X	+	X	-	X	Pseudo Diff.
14	X	X	+	-	X	Pseudo Diff.

The reference voltage fed to the V.REF pin controls the full range sensitivity of the device. The full range value is achieved at whatever voltage is used as the reference potential. This voltage must be in the range 0 to 5 volts, but for good results it should not be much less than about 1 volt. For some purposes the reference voltage can simply be provided by the +5 volt supply, or can be a fraction of this supply obtained via a simple potential divider.

Neither method is particularly satisfactory in precision measurement applications because the +5 volt rail is not likely to be highly stable or noise-free. The stability of most PC +5 volt rails is not actually all that bad, but for a critical application such as using an analogue to digital converter for accurate measurements, very well stabilised reference voltages are often needed. One method of using the device, which avoids the need for a highly stable reference voltage, is the ratiometric method. This is where the input voltages are derived from potential dividers across the +5 volt supply, as in Figure 2.20. Although the potentiometers are shown as being presets in Figure 2.20, in reality they could be ordinary potentiometers, or even potential dividers having a fixed resistor for one element, and a thermistor or some other type of sensor as the other element. The +5 volt rail is used as the reference voltage. The point about this method is that any change in the supply voltage will affect both the reference potential and the input potential. The two changes cancel out one another, giving no change in readings. Where a highly stable reference voltage is needed, any of the many low-voltage reference generator chips should be suitable. These give highly stable reference voltages, which have excellent temperature stability.

The -INTR pin is a status output. The conversion process is not an instant process, or even a particularly fast one. The ADC0844 is fairly average in terms of its conversion time, which is typically about $30\mu s$ at 25 degrees Celsius. Obviously data must not be read from the device prematurely, as invalid data would then be obtained. One method of avoiding this problem, and one which usually works well in practice, is to simply have a timing loop to provide a delay between issuing each start conversion signal and reading the converter. If necessary, some experimentation can be used in order to find the optimum delay time (i.e. the shortest delay which gives reliable operation). Bear in mind that if you are using a fairly slow computer language, such as an interpreted BASIC, you may well find that you can not read the device prematurely. With the speed of modern PCs this is by no means certain though, and delay loops are now often required in situations where they would have been unnecessary in the past.

An alternative to using a time delay is to have an input line to read the -INTR output. This is normally high, and goes low when a conversion has been completed. The hold-off would then be obtained by monitoring -INTR using a simple loop routine, and only permitting the converter to be read once -INTR had gone low. Incidentally, -INTR is reset automatically when the converter is read. There is a slight problem with this method in that an input line is required. If the analogue to digital converter is part of a large interface card, then there may well be a spare input somewhere that can be used. However, if it is on a simple ADC card, there will probably be no spare lines that can be used. Clearly, adding an 8255 in order to read one line would be using the proverbial "sledgehammer to crack a nut", and using a 74LS245 to provide one line would not be much better. A more practical approach is to use a device such as the 74LS125, which can provide up to four input lines. Figure 2.21 shows how this device can be used as a quad input port. Of course, if you only need one input line, you can use one of the buffers and ignore the other three. However, it is not a bad idea to implement all four lines, since the spare inputs might turn out to be useful for something.

There is a third option, which is to use the -INTR output to generate an interrupt. This is not difficult from the hardware point of view, but you need to be fairly expert at PC programming in order to handle this type of thing. In an application of this

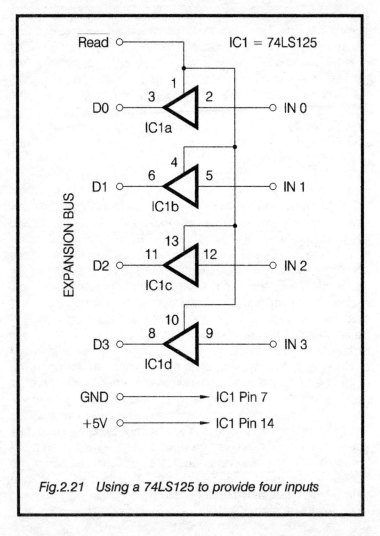

Fig.2.21 Using a 74LS125 to provide four inputs

type it is not normally necessary to resort to using interrupts. It is only likely to be worthwhile doing so in applications that are processor intensive, and where it would therefore be unacceptable to have the processor idling away waiting for

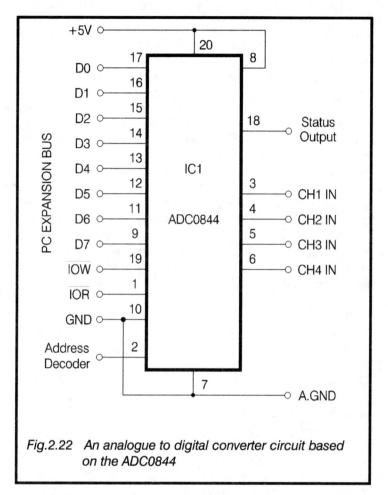

Fig.2.22 An analogue to digital converter circuit based on the ADC0844

conversions to be completed. Few applications for analogue to digital converters fall into this category. Mostly a set of readings are read and stored in memory, and they are only processed once a full set has been gathered, and no more readings will be taken. In some cases readings are taken and immediately displayed on the screen, which is not usually very demanding on the microprocessor.

Figure 2.22 shows the circuit diagram for an analogue to digital converter based on the ADC0844, complete with details of the connections to the PC expansion bus. This circuit uses the +5 volt supply as the reference voltage. Remember that the address decoder should be a type that does not decode -IOR and -IOW, as these are dealt with by the ADC0844. This circuit does not utilize the -INTR status output, and my preference is to simply use a delay loop if there is a danger of taking readings too frequently.

One final point is that the ADC0844 usually has a suffix to the basic type number. The suffix indicates the case style and operating temperature range of the component. You are most likely to see the ADC0844CCN advertised in component catalogues, and this is the version I used. Any version of the device should be satisfactory for normal purposes though.

Finally

With the information provided here, anyone with a reasonable amount of experience at electronics construction should be able to interface a wide range of devices to the PC's ISA expansion bus without too much difficulty. PC interfacing is really very straightforward, and is actually much easier than interfacing to most of the eight bit computers I have dealt with (which includes practically all the popular eight bit machines). Complications can arise if wait states have to be added, but in my experience this has never been necessary. The PC expansion bus is not particularly fast, and most peripheral chips seem to be able to keep up with it. If you end up trying to add wait states, you are probably doing things the hard way, and might be better advised to have a complete rethink.

Some applications might require the added complication of using interrupts, but there are probably few PC add-ons where the use of interrupts is essential. This is a subject that is more a matter of software than hardware, and so it will not be pursued further here. Interrupts on the PC are less fraught than on most eight-bit computers, but you still need to be fairly expert at the software side of things. You have to get things just right or each time the add-on is activated it will crash the computer. Probably the best advice when designing PC add-ons is to use sensible choices for the chips that actually interface onto the expansion bus. There are plenty of integrated circuits that will easily interface with the PCs, which means that there is probably no point in using any devices that prove to be awkward.

Chapter 3

PRINTER PORT INTERFACING

While it has to be admitted that interfacing direct onto the PC expansion bus is in many ways the best approach, as we have seen in chapters one and two, it is also slightly awkward. It requires the use of custom printed circuit boards which must be accurately made (and of the double-sided variety), or projects based on proprietary prototyping cards. This second method is relatively straightforward, but it does not necessarily produce a very neat finished product, and the prototyping cards are not particularly cheap. So is there a simpler way of connecting user add-ons to a PC? I suppose that this is a "how long is a piece of string?" style question. With some types of add-on circuit there is probably no realistic alternative to using the expansion slots. For example, if vast numbers of input/output lines are required, either a custom interface card must be produced, or your add-on must interface via a ready-made multi-line interface card. With many of the more simple and straightforward projects though, the standard PC ports often offer a practical (and easier) alternative to the expansion bus.

Printer Port
There are three types of standard PC port that are potentially usable for your own add-ons. These are the serial, parallel, and analogue ports. Interfacing via a serial port is not particularly difficult, and the serial-to-parallel and parallel-to-serial conversion is easily achieved using a UART (universal asynchronous receiver/transmitter). In most cases it is easier to use a parallel port, but for those who prefer the serial approach this topic is covered in the next chapter. Obviously most PCs have a printer port connected to a printer, and this port is therefore unavailable for general use unless you resort to some form of "printer sharer" switching device. On the other hand, many PCs have a second printer port, and in most cases this is left totally unused. Even if

a second port is not fitted, a very inexpensive expansion card is all that is needed in order to equip your computer with a second port.

Although a printer port may seem to be of limited use for general interfacing purposes, the PC printer ports are actually quite versatile. On the face of it a parallel printer port is an output type, and it has little or no potential for use as an input port. Fortunately, in addition to the eight data outputs a PC printer port has several handshake lines. In fact there are no less than nine of these - five inputs and four outputs. As we shall see later in this chapter, the handshake lines enable the port to act as an input or output type, or both at once. Some external circuitry is required in order to make the port function as an eight-bit input type, but it only requires a very simple and inexpensive add-on.

Obtaining eight inputs and eight output lines using one of the printer ports is certainly much easier than using a serial port or the expansion bus to provide the same function. Also, the parallel port can read and write at a much higher rate, and it still has some spare lines for general handshaking purposes or other uses. One possible use for these extra lines is to provide further 8 bit input or output ports. It is actually possible to obtain a large number of input and output lines using a printer port and basic multiplexing techniques. For complex interfacing of this type I would be inclined to opt for a proper multi-port expansion card, but the printer port method is perfectly feasible if that is the approach you prefer.

Advantages
So why should you bother to use the PC's printer ports for general interfacing when there is a perfectly good expansion bus? As already pointed out, there are practical difficulties in using the expansion slots, making it a rather awkward prospect for the average electronics hobbyist. The printer and joystick ports are much more straightforward, and provide no real

difficulties. You simply connect your add-on to the PC via a multi-way lead terminated in the appropriate type of D connector. Even if you are equipped to make accurate double-sided printed circuit boards, the relative simplicity of interfacing to the PC's built-in interfaces could reasonably be regarded as a more attractive proposition. It is noticeable that an increasing range of ready-made PC add-ons is designed to connect to the built-in interfaces rather than the expansion bus.

Another advantage of the built-in ports is that they effectively provide you with some of the hardware for your add-ons, but at little or no cost. At little cost if you need to buy an expansion card to provide the printer of "games" port, or no cost if your computer is supplied complete with suitable ports (as most are). If you interface via the expansion slots it is necessary to include address decoding and input/output ports on the card. This means that you end up with a fair amount of circuitry before you start on the project itself! Using the built-in ports means that all or most of the basic interfacing is taken care of for you.

On the face of it there is an advantage in using the expansion slots for your add-ons, as it keeps everything neat and tidy with your circuits tucked away inside the PC. In reality things are usually slightly less straightforward than this. You often seem to end up with projects that are half on the expansion card and half outside the computer, with a big lead between the two. This is because you often need to have access to the add-on. For example, EPROM programming and chip testing requires you to be able to plug chips into the add-on unit. If a project has any controls, these must be on an external unit so that you can get at them. With projects of these types, using the built-in ports would seem to be no more or less neat than using the expansion slots. It is likely to be significantly less expensive though.

Using the integral ports does have one or two drawbacks. I suppose one of these drawbacks is that it is ultimately more limiting than using the expansion slots, but this is obviously irrelevant unless you intend to do some fairly complex interfacing. For many purposes the built-in ports are perfectly adequate. Another slight drawback is that there are no power rails available on the printer ports. Only a +5 volt rail is available when using the "games" port. When using the printer ports it is possible to use the "games" or keyboard port to provide a +5 volt supply, which is all that many add-ons require. At the time of writing this, USB (universal serial bus) ports are still relatively rare. They are actually present on the motherboards of many PCs, but relatively few are equipped with connectors at the rear of the case to enable these ports to be connected to the outside world. Anyway, if your PC does have an unused USB port, this is another potential source of a +5 volt supply. When using the printer ports or "games" port it is possible to use the expansion bus as a source for all the PC's supply rails. However, this is not a particularly neat solution, and if anything beyond a simple +5 volt supply is needed, it is normal practice to provide the add-on with its own power supply unit.

Right Lines
The PC printer connector is a female 25 way D type connector. You therefore need a male 25 way D connector to make the connections to each port. When used for their intended purpose the pins of each printer port have the functions detailed in Figure 3.1. This shows the port as viewed from the outside of the computer. Looking at it another way, it shows the pin functions of the male connector as viewed from rear. In other words, as viewed when you are actually making the connections to the plug. If you are unsure about the pin numbering of practically any computer connector, it is worth bearing in mind that virtually all of these connectors have the pin numbers marked on the connectors themselves. Unfortunately, the small size of most connectors inevitably means that the lettering is very small. In the case of D type connectors, matters are not helped by the

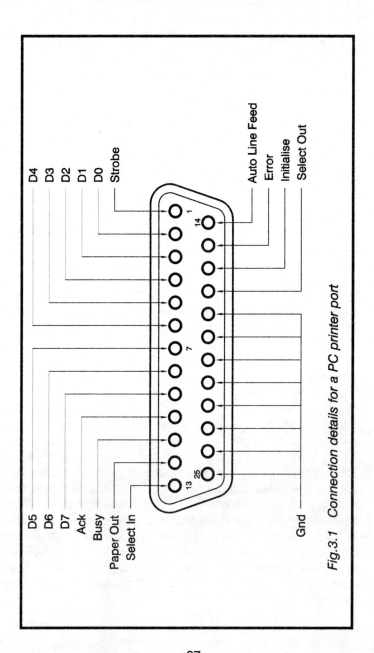

Fig.3.1   Connection details for a PC printer port

fact that the numbers are moulded into the plastic body of the connectors. You may well need the aid of a magnifier to read the numbers, but this is a certain method of avoiding a set of "mirrored" connections to the D plugs.

One way of using a printer port for general interfacing is to make your add-on circuit mimic a parallel printer, so that data can be written to it in the normal way. This method does have possible advantages, since there are operating system routines and general high level support to control the flow of data to the port. If you interface to the port in the normal way, there should be no difficulty in using these routines and support. The drawback of this method is that it is very restrictive, and only permits the port to operate as a fairly basic eight-bit output type. This aspect of things is covered in more detail in the final chapter of this book.

Direct control of the printer ports permits much greater versatility, and in conjunction with some external hardware makes it possible to have numerous input and output lines. Even if you do wish to use the printer as nothing more than an eight bit output with handshaking, it might still be easier to write direct to the port, and control the flow of data using your own software routines. This type of thing is not particularly complex, and is easily integrated with the main program. I would certainly recommend direct control of the ports wherever possible. When taking direct control of the printer ports is best to largely forget the intended purposes of the input lines. The exception here are the eight data outputs ("D0" to "D7" in Figure 3.1). These are eight latching outputs, and it is to these that bytes of data are written when the ports are used to drive printers. Their function is normally the same when they are used for general interfacing purposes. The only difference when they are used for general interfacing is that you write data to the appropriate input/output address, and not to a DOS device via the operating system.

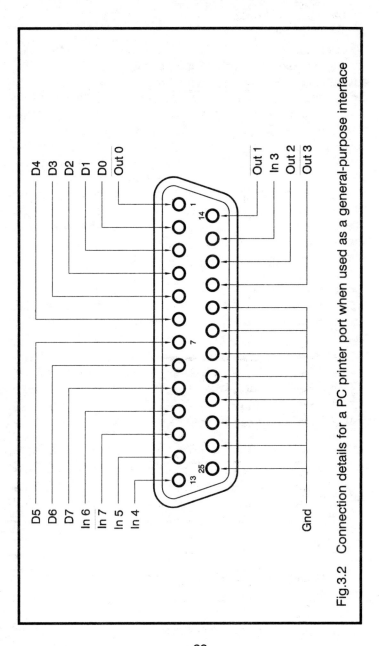

D4
D3
D2
D1
D0
Out 0

D5
D6
D7
In 6
In 7
In 5
In 4

Out 1
In 3
Out 2
Out 3

Gnd

1
14
7
13 25

Fig.3.2 Connection details for a PC printer port when used as a general-purpose interface

With the other lines their original functions should be forgotten, and they should be thought of as input and output lines at certain addresses in the PC's input/output map. Figure 3.2 shows the pin functions with this alternative way of viewing things. As will be apparent from this diagram, in addition to the eight bit output there are four other outputs, and five input lines. Unfortunately, some of these additional inputs and outputs have built-in inverters. These are the ones which have the line marked over the pin function. This is generally a bit inconvenient, but the inverters do not place any major limitations on the ways in which the relevant lines can be used. Where the inversions are not needed they can be counteracted by using external inverters in your interface circuit. Alternatively, the software routines can be written to take into account any unwanted inversions.

Properly Addressed
In DOS terminology the printer ports are LPT1 and LPT2. They each occupy three addresses in the PC's input/output map. Note that the 8088 series of microprocessors used in the PCs have separate memory and input/output maps, and the printer ports are obviously in the input/output map. When writing data to one of these ports, or reading from them, you must therefore use instructions that are appropriate to input/output devices. Thus, in GW BASIC you would use INP and OUT, not PEEK and POKE. The normal scheme of things is for LPT1 to be at addresses from &H378 to &H37A, and LPT2 to be at addresses from &H278 to &H27A. The decimal equivalents for these hexadecimal address ranges are 888 to 890, and 632 to 634. In this book we will deal in hexadecimal addresses, but when writing software for use with your own printer port add-ons it is obviously in order to use decimal addresses if this is your preferred way of doing things.

This table shows the location of each printer port input/output line in the PC's input/output map.

I/O Line Address Mapping

LPT2

&H278

Bit	Line
0	D0
1	D1
2	D2
3	D3
4	D4
5	D5
6	D6
7	D7

&H279

Bit	Line
0	unused
1	unused
2	unused
3	In 3
4	In 4
5	In 5
6	In 6
7	In 7 (inverted)

&H27A

Bit	Line
0	Out 0 (inverted)
1	Out 1 (inverted)
2	Out 2
3	Out 3 (inverted)
4	unused
5	unused or direction
6	unused
7	unused

LPT1

&H378

Bit	Line
0	D0
1	D1
2	D2
3	D3
4	D4
5	D5
6	D6
7	D7

&H379

Bit	Line
0	unused
1	unused
2	unused
3	In 3
4	In 4
5	In 5
6	In 6
7	In 7 (inverted)

&H37A

Bit	Line
0	Out 0 (inverted)
1	Out 1 (inverted)
2	Out 2
3	Out 3 (inverted)
4	unused or direction
5	unused
6	unused
7	unused

There is a slight complication in that a third address block is sometimes used for PC printer ports. These addresses are &H3BC, &H3BD, and &H3BE. This address range seems to have its origins in the original Hercules graphics adapter, which included a parallel port. It is still used to some extent today, and many modern PCs can be set to use this address range via the BIOS Setup program. Apparently some PCs are supplied with this set as the address range for the built-in printer port. Where this address range is in use the operating system will probably use it for LPT1, with any ports at &H378 or &H278 being moved one port number higher as a result. If you are controlling the ports directly this is not of any great significance, but you must obviously use the correct address range for the port in question. The BIOS will normally show a list of the base addresses for all the ports during the start-up routine, and this may tell you what you need to know. If not, you can always resort to trial and error to find the address range to which a port responds.

Writing to the eight data lines of either port is very straightforward, and it is just a matter of writing the correct value to the appropriate address. For example, to set all eight data lines of LPT2 high a value of 255 would be written to address &H278. In GW BASIC or Q BASIC this would achieved using the OUT instruction (i.e. OUT &H278,255). There is no need to include data latches in your add-on circuits, because the data outputs are latching types.

Presumably due to the fact that some commercial peripherals for PCs use the printer port for bidirectional parallel interfacing, many people seem to have gained the impression that the data lines of any PC printer port can be used as inputs or outputs. The input mode is not possible using a standard PC printer port, and can only be achieved using a bidirectional type. However, many recent printer port cards are of the bidirectional variety, as are virtually all built-in PC printer ports of PCs that are no more than a few years old. Bidirectional operation is considered in detail at the end of this chapter.

Like the data outputs, the four handshake outputs at addresses &H27A and &H37A are latching types, and they can only act as outputs. Again, it is just a matter of writing the appropriate value to the port address. With handshake lines it would usually be easier if they could be operated entirely independently. This is clearly not possible here, because all four handshake outputs of each printer port are at the same address. Therefore, when altering the state of one output, great care must be taken not to alter the states of the other three outputs.

A standard way of achieving this is to read from the port to determine the states of the outputs, and then work out a modified value to write back to the port, so that only the desired change is made. This is not a reliable method in this case, since this is a write-only address. You can not be sure that the values read back will accurately reflect the states of the outputs. In fact it is highly unlikely that they would, and with most printer port cards a value of 255 will always be returned from the handshake output address. This is simply because no hardware is actually activated by a read operation to the handshake output addresses, and the data lines of the microprocessor are left free to drift. They all drift to the high state, giving a returned value of 255. Where necessary, your software routines must therefore be carefully written so that the program "remembers" the last value written to the handshake outputs.

Of course, with only four of the bits at each of these addresses actually used, only data values from 0 to 15 are valid. Values from 16 to 255 will not cause a software error, but only the least significant four bits of these values will affect the states of the handshake outputs. For instance, a value of 16 would set all four outputs low, and a value of 255 would set them all high. On the other hand, it would not be good programming practice to write out-of-range values to a port.

Quart into A Pint Port

One the face of it, the handshake inputs are only suitable for their intended purpose, since five inputs is not enough to read in bytes of data. In reality they can be used to read in bytes of data, but this requires a small amount of additional hardware, plus one of the handshake outputs. It is just a matter of using some basic multiplexing, and Figure 3.3 shows the basic set-up used. Four of the handshake inputs are fed from two sets of four bit tristate buffers. The handshake output directly drives the enable input of one quad tristate buffer, but drives the enable input of the other via an inverter. Only one or other of the quad buffers will be active at any one time, and the required buffer can be selected by setting the handshake output to the appropriate state.

The lower nibble of the eight-bit input is applied to one buffer, and the upper nibble is applied to the other buffer. In order to read in a complete byte it is necessary to read the two nibbles separately and then use a simple software routine to combine the two readings in such a way that the correct value for the full byte is obtained. This method is obviously not as quick and direct as reading data in complete bytes, but even with a fairly slow PC it would probably be possible to read in a few hundred thousand bytes per second. It is certainly faster than using the serial ports, which enable data to be read at no more than a few kilobytes per second.

There is a potential problem though, and this is that the byte of data being read might change in the period between the first and second nibbles being read. This is a problem that exists with any input method that provides something less than instant reading of a port. Where necessary, the problem must be dealt with using conventional handshake methods. For example, a handshake output could be used to latch input bytes into a data latch. The input port would then be used to read the bytes of data "frozen" in the data latch, rather than reading the bytes of data directly. Of course, in many cases the input data will change too slowly to create a major problem. However, even where the data changes relatively slowly it might be as well to use a software routine to check for inaccurate readings. For example, readings can be taken until three consecutive values are the same. This does not absolutely guarantee glitch-free results, but in practice would probably be sufficient to prevent any spurious readings.

Options

There is more than one way of interfacing this type of input port to the PC. Perhaps the obvious way is to drive the four most significant handshake lines from the quad buffers. The basic port reading process would then follow along these general lines. First the handshake output would be used to select the least significant nibble, and the port would be read. The returned value would then be placed into a variable. Next the handshake output would be used to select the most significant nibble, and a reading would be taken. This reading would then be stored in a second variable. The value returned from the most significant nibble is correct, and needs no mathematical manipulation. The same is not true of the least significant nibble, which has been read in on the four most significant input lines. In order to make a correction for this it is merely necessary to divide the stored value by sixteen. Adding this value to the one read from the most significant nibble then gives the full value for the byte. In practice there is a slight problem with this method in that bit 7 is inverted. This is not a major problem as it can be corrected by using an inverter ahead of this input. Alternatively, further software could be used to invert this bit.

It is possible to avoid the problem of the inversion on bit seven by using bits three to six instead of bits four to seven. There are no internal inverters on bits three to six. The port reading process is much the same as before, with the most and least significant nibbles being read, and the returned values being placed into variables. The mathematical manipulation is

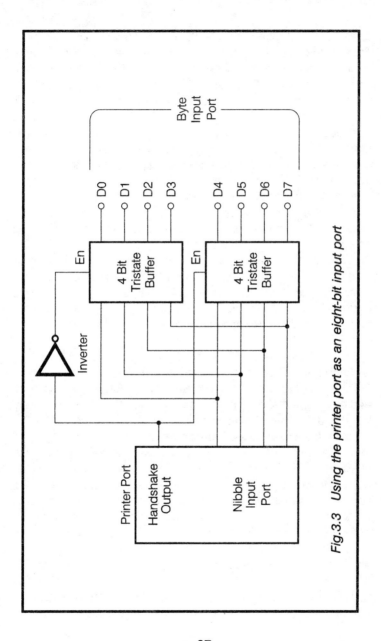

Fig.3.3   Using the printer port as an eight-bit input port

obviously a bit different. This time the most significant nibble does require some correction, and this is achieved by simply multiplying it by two. A division by eight corrects the least significant nibble. Then, as before, the two values are added together to give the value for the complete byte.

It does not matter which of the four handshake outputs is used to control the quad tristate buffers. If there are two unused handshake outputs it is possible to dispense with the inverter. Instead, each buffer is controlled from a separate handshake output, and the software controls these in such a way that only one or other of the buffers is ever active at any one time. Of course, with this method a programming error could result in both buffers being active simultaneously, and some careful programming would be needed in order to avoid this. There is also a potential problem with both buffers being activated at switch-on, prior to your controlling software being run. This might not have disastrous results, but my preferred method is to include the inverter and use a single handshake output.

Using the method of interfacing outlined here it is possible for each printer port to provide an eight bit latching output port, an eight bit input port, plus two or three handshake outputs, and one handshake input. This is sufficient for many purposes, but it is actually possible to have further expansion per port if desired. In the same way that eight input lines can be multiplexed into four input lines, 16 input lines can be multiplexed into those eight lines. This is just a matter of using two eight bit tristate buffers to provide the additional multiplexing, plus one of the spare handshake outputs to control the buffers. Things could be taken a stage further, but multiplexing beyond 16 input lines produces a relatively complex circuit, and requires some convoluted programming in order to read the ports. My advice would be to use a proper parallel expansion card if large numbers of inputs are required. This is likely to be a more expensive way of tackling things, but it would also be a very much more straightforward and convenient solution to the problem.

Multiplexing techniques can also be applied to the eight data outputs, enabling two or more eight bit output ports to be provided. Again, trying to provide numerous ports in this way is probably not very practical, and a proper parallel expansion card would then be a better option. Providing two or three ports in this way is reasonably straightforward though.

Input Port
Having looked at the basic principles behind interfacing to the printer ports we will now consider some practical circuits for input ports, and multiple input and output ports. We will start with basic eight bit input ports. There are numerous ways of providing the required multiplexing, and the best method is largely dependent on the way in which the port will be used. In most cases it will not matter which method is used, and it is then just a matter of selecting the one that you find the most convenient. Here we will look at one solution that is suitable for most practical applications.

The circuit of Figure 3.4 is for an input port, which drives handshake, inputs from D3 to D6. This is the method I generally prefer, since it avoids the complication of the inversion on bit 7. There are various tristate buffers that can be used in this application, and in this circuit a 74LS244 octal tristate buffer is used. Although this chip is normally described as an octal buffer, it is in fact two four bit types having separate enable inputs. This makes it ideal for use in the present application. IC2 provides an inversion so that the two halves of IC1 are driven in anti-phase. Any of the four handshake outputs could be used to control the buffers, but to keep things as straightforward as possible the strobe output (bit 0 at pin 1 of the port) is used. The least significant nibble is read when pin 1 is low - the most significant nibble is read when pin 1 is high. However, bear in mind that there is a built-in inversion on the strobe output, so this output is set high and low using values of 0 and 1 respectively. This simple GW BASIC routine will read the port and print the returned value on the screen. This is for an interface

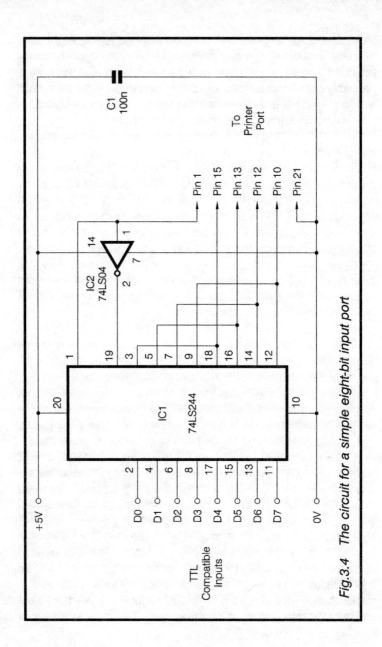

Fig.3.4 The circuit for a simple eight-bit input port

on LPT1, but with the appropriate addresses it will also work with an interface on LPT2. The program should work using any BASIC that is compatible with GW BASIC, including Q BASIC.

```
5  REM PROG TO READ IN BYTE ON BITS 3 TO 6
10 OUT &H37A,1
20 LSN = INP(&H379) AND 120
30 LSN = LSN/8
40 OUT &H37A,0
50 MSN = INP(&H379) AND 120
60 MSN = MSN * 2
70 BYTE = LSN + MSN
80 PRINT BYTE
```

Line 10 sets the control output low so that the least significant nibble is selected. This nibble is then read at line 20 and placed in the variable called "LSN". The value read from the port is bitwise ANDed with a value of 120 so that only bits three to six are read, and the other four bits are masked. The bitwise ANDing process is described in detail in the chapter that deals with software matters. Those who are unfamiliar with this procedure would be well advised to study the relevant section of this book, since it is difficult to undertake anything more than some very basic computer interfacing without a proper understanding of bitwise ANDing.

The value held in LSN is incorrect, as the wrong lines (i.e. bits three to six instead of zero to three) have read it. When working in assembly language this type of thing can be handled using rotate or shift instructions to move the bits into the correct positions. When using a high level language it is easier to use multiplication or division to correct the positioning of bits. In this case a division by eight at line 30 produces the correct value for the least significant nibble. At line 40 the control output is set high so that the most significant nibble is selected. This nibble is then read at line 50, and the returned value is placed in a variable called "MSN". The value of this nibble is corrected at

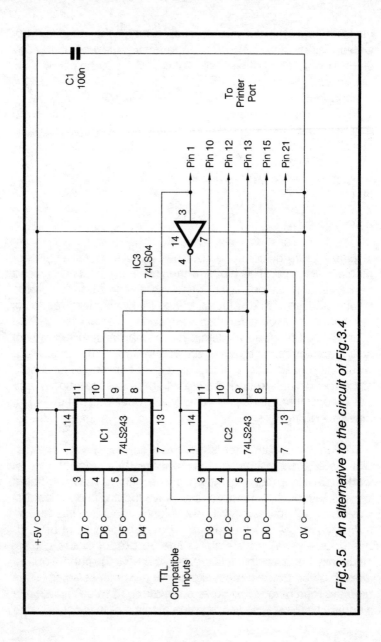

Fig.3.5   An alternative to the circuit of Fig.3.4

line 60 where it is multiplied by two. Finally, the values of the two nibbles are added together to produce the full eight-bit value, which is placed in the variable called "BYTE", and printed on the screen.

Although this single-chip solution to the tristate buffering looks very neat on paper, in reality it is something less than simplicity itself. The problem is simply that the pinout configuration of the 74LS244 is not as convenient as it might be. This is not a major problem if you have the necessary facilities to produce intricate printed circuit boards, but it makes life difficult if you are only able to produce relatively simple boards, or you wish to use a proprietary printed circuit board such as stripboard. For construction using stripboard, etc., the alternative circuit of Figure 3.5 should prove to be a better choice. This is based on two 74LS243 quad transceivers, but in this circuit both devices are connected to act as quad tristate buffers. The 74LS243 conveniently has all the inputs in one row of pins, and all the outputs in the other row. This makes it much easier to design a suitable component layout, particularly when using stripboard and other proprietary printed circuit boards.

The control input at pin 1 of each device is connected to the +5 volt rail, and the other control input at pin 13 of each chip then gives standard tristate control (high to enable the outputs, or low to disable them). As before, an inverter (IC3) is used to provide the required anti-phase control of the tristate buffers. Like the circuit of Figure 3.4, the control input must be low to read the least significant nibble, and high to read the most significant nibble. Therefore, the GW BASIC routine provided previously will also work with this version of the input port.

Dual Inputs
It is not difficult to use the printer port's handshake lines to provide two eight bit input ports, and it is just a matter of using additional multiplexing controlled by one of the spare handshake outputs. Figure 3.6 shows one way of providing the additional

103

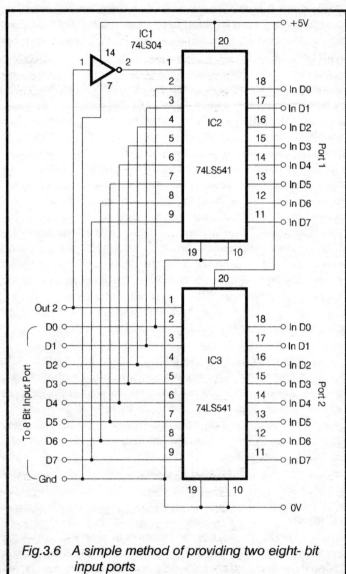

Fig.3.6 A simple method of providing two eight- bit
input ports

104

multiplexing. Note that this circuit requires an eight bit input port, and that it must therefore be added onto one of the input ports described previously. It can not be used straight onto the printer port because the unaided printer port has an insufficient number of inputs. Of course, the situation is different if your PC has a bidirectional printer port, and doubling the number of inputs available from a bidirectional port is covered in the relevant section of this chapter.

The circuit is based on two 74LS541 8 bit tristate buffers. Their inputs act as the two eight bit input ports, and their outputs drive the basic eight bit input port. IC3 is controlled direct from "Out 2" of the printer port (the "Initialise" handshake output), but IC2 is controlled via an inverter. If the basic input port uses one or two inverters, IC1 can be an unused section of the 74LS04 used in the basic input port circuit. The inversion provided by IC1 provides the required anti-phase operation of the buffers, with IC2 enabled when "Out 2" is high, and IC3 enabled when "Out 2" is low.

The 74LS541 actually has a two input AND gate ahead of its active low enable input. The inputs of the gate are accessible at pins 1 and 19. The gating is not required in this case, so pin 19 is connected to the 0-volt rail, and pin 1 is used as a straightforward negative enable input. If it suits the component layout better, connect pin 1 to ground and use pin 19 as the control input. The circuit provides exactly the same action either way.

Obviously the way in which the dual port is read depends on the input port circuit utilized. For the sake of this example we will assume that it is connected to an input port of the type featured in Figure 3.4, 3.5, or an exact equivalent of these. If you use a different method of interfacing to the handshake inputs this routine will have to be amended accordingly. This routine will read port 1 and print the returned value on the screen.
5 REM PROG TO READ PORT 1

```
10 OUT &H37A,5
20 LSN = INP(&H379) AND 120
30 LSN = LSN/8
40 OUT &H37A,4
50 MSN = INP(&H379) AND 120
60 MSN = MSN * 2
70 BYTE = LSN + MSN
80 PRINT BYTE
```

This operates in exactly the same way as the program to read the basic input port, but lines 10 and 40 have been modified to take "Out 2" high, so that IC2 is activated and port 1 is selected. Remember that "Out 2", unlike the other three handshake outputs, does not have a built-in inversion. It is therefore set high using a value of 4, and low using a value of 0. This version of the program sets "Out 2" low so that port 2 is read.

```
5  REM PROG TO READ PORT 2
10 OUT &H37A,1
20 LSN = INP(&H379) AND 120
30 LSN = LSN/8
40 OUT &H37A,0
50 MSN = INP(&H379) AND 120
60 MSN = MSN * 2
70 BYTE = LSN + MSN
80 PRINT BYTE
```

Figure 3.7 shows the circuit for an alternative dual input circuit. This is based on two 74LS245 octal transceivers, which seem to be a bit easier to obtain than the 74LS541 tristate buffers. IC1 and IC2 are both hard wired into the "receive" mode by having pin 1 connected to ground. This effectively downgrades them to simple tristate buffers, controlled via the negative chip enable input at pin 19 of each device. Consequently, this circuit is functionally the same as that of Figure 3.6, and can be controlled using the same software routines.

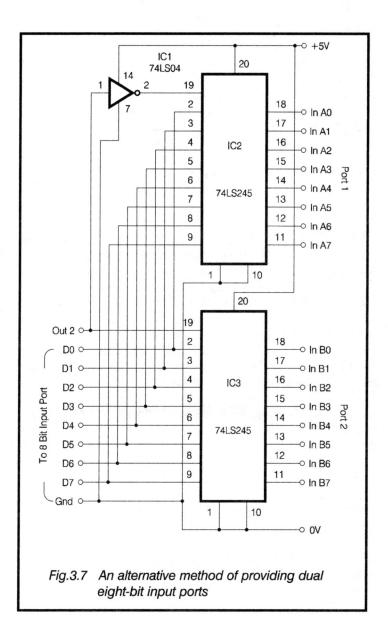

Fig.3.7   An alternative method of providing dual eight-bit input ports

107

Grabbing Bytes

As pointed out previously, reading in bytes of data as two separate nibbles can cause problems when the data is changing fairly rapidly. A change between the first and second nibbles being read could produce completely erroneous results. This problem can be overcome by using an eight bit data latch to "freeze" complete bytes which can then be read by one of the eight bit input ports. This is the digital equivalent of an analogue sample-and-hold circuit. Data latching does not require much additional circuitry, but it does require an extra handshake output to control the data latch. Figure 3.8 shows one way of providing data latching.

IC1 is a 74LS373 octal "transparent" latch. When its control input at pin 11 is taken high, the binary pattern on the inputs is simply transferred straight through to the outputs. Taking pin 11 low "freezes" the outputs, and latches them with the data present on the inputs as pin 11 made the high-to-low transition. In this example pin 11 of IC1 is controlled by "Out 2", but it could be controlled by any spare handshake output. This GW BASIC program will latch data into IC1 and then read it. Again, for the sake of this example we will assume that the input port circuit of Figure 3.4 or 3.5 is being used.

```
10 REM PROG TO READ BYTE VIA DATA LATCH (74LS373)
20 OUT &H37A,0
30 OUT &H37A,4
40 OUT &H37A,0
45 FOR DELAY = 1 TO 30000: NEXT DELAY
50 OUT &H37A,1
60 LSN = INP(&H379) AND 120
70 LSN = LSN/8
80 OUT &H37A,0
90 MSN = INP(&H379) AND 120
100 MSN = MSN * 2
110 BYTE = LSN + MSN
120 PRINT BYTE
```

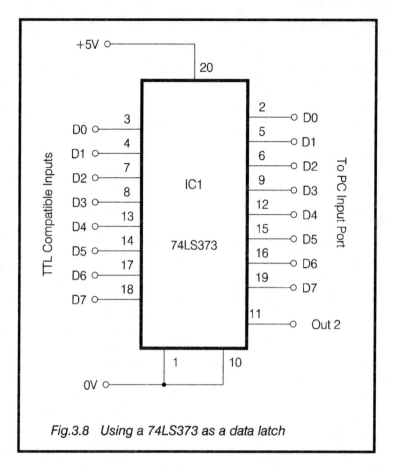

Fig.3.8   Using a 74LS373 as a data latch

This is just the normal port reading routine, but with lines 20 to 40 added to provide a positive latching pulse prior to the port being read. It is at line 40, where "Out 2" goes through a high-to-low transition, that the data is latched into the 74LS373. Line 45 is not part of the reading routine, and it simply provides a delay between the latching pulse and the latched data being read. This gives you an opportunity to alter the input data during this in-between period, so that the effectiveness of the latching

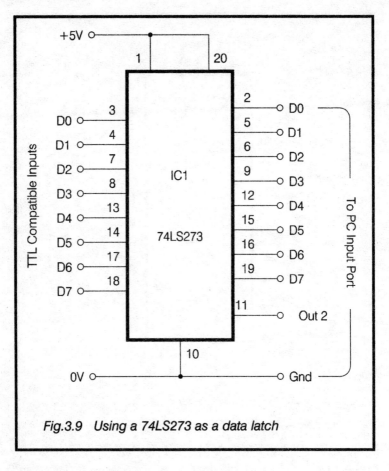

Fig.3.9 Using a 74LS273 as a data latch

can be checked. Obviously in normal use this line should be omitted.

Figure 3.9 shows an alternative data latch circuit. This is based on a 74LS273, which is an octal D type flip/flop. It works as a data latch if pin 11 is normally held high and is briefly pulsed low in order to latch a fresh byte of data. It is on the low-to-high transition that the data on the outputs is "frozen". Unlike the

110

74LS373, the 74LS273 is never "transparent". Data can only be transferred from the inputs to the outputs by using the latching process. Note also, that control of the 74LS273 is the opposite way round to the 74LS373, with a low pulse being used to latch the data. This circuit therefore needs slightly modified control software. The following GW BASIC program will latch data into the 74LS273 and then read it.

```
10 REM PROG TO READ BYTE VIA DATA LATCH (74LS273)
20 OUT &H37A,4
30 OUT &H37A,0
40 OUT &H37A,4
45 FOR DELAY = 1 TO 30000: NEXT DELAY
50 OUT &H37A,1
60 LSN = INP(&H379) AND 120
70 LSN = LSN/8
80 OUT &H37A,0
90 MSN = INP(&H379) AND 120
100 MSN = MSN * 2
110 BYTE = LSN + MSN
120 PRINT BYTE
```

Dual Outputs

The eight data outputs of the printer port (D0 to D5 in Figures 3.1 and 3.2) provide a ready-made eight bit output port. This makes writing bytes of data much easier than reading them, since it is possible to write complete bytes. Simply write the appropriate value to input/output address &H378 (LPT1) or &H278 (LPT2) and the data lines will take up the correct binary pattern. There are no inversions on any of these lines, and they are all TTL compatible.

Using the single eight bit output to provide two eight bit outputs is very simple, and it requires nothing more than a couple of data latches, with each one controlled from a separate handshake output. Figure 3.10 shows one way of providing an extra output port. This uses two 74LS273 octal D type flip/flops

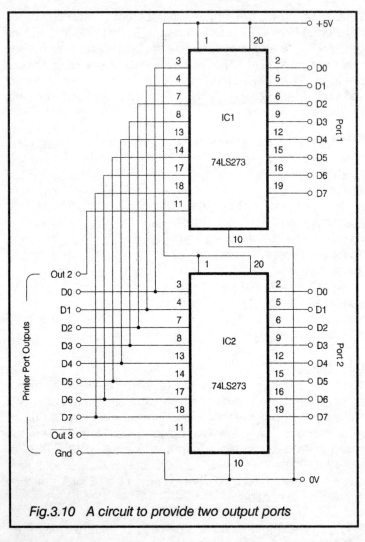

Fig.3.10   A circuit to provide two output ports

as the data latches. The handshake control lines are normally
held in the high state. In order to write a byte of data to port 1
the data is first written to the data lines of the printer port. The

handshake line used to control IC1 ("Out 2" in this example) is then taken low and high again. On the low-to-high transition the new byte of data is latched onto IC1's outputs. Data is written to port 2 in much the same way, but it is handshake line "Out 3" that is pulsed low in order to latch the new byte of data onto the outputs of port 2.

The negative reset inputs of IC1 and IC2 are simply connected to the positive supply rail so that they have no effect. If preferred, a C - R network can be used to provide a negative pulse at switch-on to ensure that all the outputs of both ports start out in the low state. This is only necessary where random values on the port outputs could have dire consequences. It might require a very long reset pulse to ensure that the computer's start-up and initial testing routines do not override the reset pulse.

The software to write data to the ports is very simple. This example in GW BASIC will write a value of 123 to port 1.

```
10 REM PROG TO WRITE A BYTE OF DATA TO PORT 1
   (74LS273 LATCHES)
20 OUT &H37A,4
30 OUT &H378,123
40 OUT &H37A,0
50 OUT &H378,4
```

Line 20 sets the handshake outputs at their correct initial states, which is with both of them in the high state. Remember that "Out 3" has a built-in inversion, and a value of zero rather than eight is therefore needed in order to set this line high. The data is written to the printer port's data lines at line 30, and then the next two lines produce a low pulse on "Out 2", while leaving "Out 3" high. It is on the low-to-high transition produced by line 50 that the fresh byte of data appears on the outputs of port 1.

Writing data to port 2 uses a similar process. This example GW BASIC routine writes a value of 231 to port 2.

```
10 REM PROG TO WRITE A BYTE OF DATA TO PORT 2
   (74LS273 LATCHES)
20 OUT &H37A,4
30 OUT &H378,231
40 OUT &H37A,12
50 OUT &H37A,4
```

Again, line 20 sets the correct initial states on the handshake outputs, and the value for port 2 is written to the printer port data lines at line 30. Lines 40 and 50 then provide a negative pulse on "Out 3", but leave "Out 2" high so that the data on the port 1 outputs is left unchanged. Of course, if it was necessary to write the same byte of data to both ports, this could be achieved by writing the data to the printer port data lines, and then pulsing both "Out 2" and "Out 3".

Figure 3.11 shows an alternative method of providing twin eight bit output ports. This operates in much the same way as the circuit of Figure 3.10, but in this case the data latches are 74LS373 octal transparent latches. The only significant difference when using this method is that the handshake outputs should normally be low, and pulsed high in order to latch data into their respective latches. This GW BASIC routine will write a value of 156 to port 1.

```
10 REM PROG TO WRITE A BYTE OF DATA TO PORT 1
   (74LS373 LATCHES)
20 OUT &H37A,8
30 OUT &H378,156
40 OUT &H37A,0
50 OUT &H37A,8
```

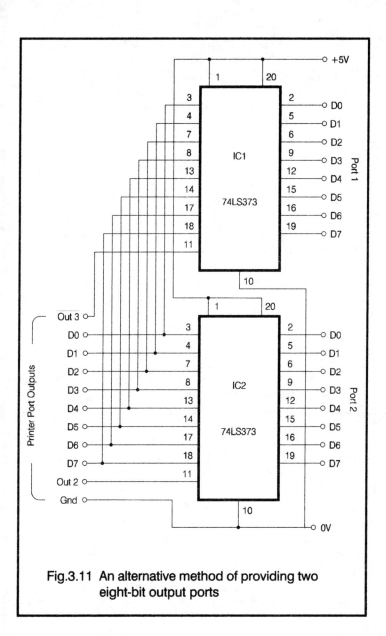

Fig.3.11 An alternative method of providing two
eight-bit output ports

This GW BASIC program will write a value of 54 to port 2.

```
10 REM PROG TO WRITE A BYTE OF DATA TO PORT
   (74LS373 LATCHES)
20 OUT &H37A,8
30 OUT &H378,56
40 OUT &H37A,4
50 OUT &H37A,8
```

Of course, with four handshake outputs available on the printer port it is possible to extend this basic scheme of things to provide three or four eight bit output ports. The only problem is that this tends to tie up the handshake outputs so that there is little scope for providing extra input lines, or for using the handshake outputs for their intended purpose. In practice it might therefore be better to opt for a proper parallel interface card if a large number of outputs are required. It is perfectly possible to provide up to 32 output lines though.

Bidirectional Operation
Most modern PC printer ports, whether built-in or provided via expansion cards, are bidirectional. In other words, the eight data lines can set to operate as inputs. It is not possible to have split operation with some lines as inputs and others as outputs. The port can only operate in the normal output mode, or with all the lines as inputs. Even so, this provides much greater versatility, and makes life much easier if you only require an eight-bit input port plus some handshake lines. There is no need to use any external hardware to achieve this; you simply set the data lines to act as inputs and make use of whichever of the nine handshake lines you require. It also makes the software side of things much easier, since bytes of data can be read in a single instruction. It is only fair to point out that in some circumstances it might be better to use the handshake inputs to read in bytes of data, rather than using the data lines. If you require eight-bit input and output ports, using the handshake

116

inputs and some hardware to provide the inputs, and the data lines to act as the outputs almost certainly represents the easiest way of doing things.

How do you determine whether or not your parallel printer ports are capable of bidirectional operation? You can simply adopt the "suck it and see" approach, but this is not as reliable as you might expect, because not all printer ports default to bidirectional operation. Also, there is more than one bidirectional mode, and the port could simply be set to the wrong one. If you are using a port provided by an expansion card you should look carefully at the instruction manual or leaflet supplied with the card. If more than one mode of operation is supported this should make it clear how each one is obtained. This will normally mean setting jumpers or DIP switches to select the required mode. There may be something like a "normal" mode, which only provides data outputs, and an SPP or EPP mode. These are the "standard parallel port" and "enhanced parallel port" modes, either of which will provide the basic two-way operation that we require.

Motherboards usually have the parallel port controlled via the BIOS Setup program. With most PCs the BIOS Setup program is entered by pressing the "Del" key at the appropriate point in the initial boot-up routine. However, there are plenty of alternative methods, and if in doubt you should consult the instruction manual for your computer or the manual for its motherboard. Modern Setup programs are quite large, and have the available options in half a dozen or so groups. The serial and parallel port settings are usually in a section called something like "Integrated Peripherals". Any EPP or SPP mode should be suitable for basic bidirectional use. With the more recent motherboards there is also likely to be an ECP (extended capabilities parallel port) mode, and although this provides a form of bidirectional operation, it does not seem to provide the basic method of control we require.

Direction Control

When set for bidirectional operation a printer port defaults to the output mode, and operates in exactly the same manner as an ordinary printer port. This is something that must be borne in mind when using the port as an input type, because it means that initially the outputs of your project will be driving the outputs of the printer port. This could lead to large currents flowing, and possible damage to the printer port or your project. Most bidirectional printer ports have current limiting on the data outputs to ensure that no damage occurs, but it is advisable to take no chances and include current limiting resistors between the outputs of your project and the printer port data lines. The values of these resistors must be high enough to ensure that only safe currents can flow, but low enough to permit the circuits to function correctly. A value of around 270R is satisfactory.

Setting the port to the input mode is easy enough, and is achieved via bit five at the handshake output address (normally &H37A for LPT1, and &H27A for LPT2). The four least significant bits of this address are used to control the handshake outputs of the port, and due care must be taken not to alter the settings of the handshake lines when setting the port to the input mode. Similarly, you must make sure that the port is not inadvertently set back to the output mode when writing data to the handshake lines. This basically just boils down to always writing 32 (decimal) more than normal to the handshake output register so that bit five is always at logic one. Also, make sure that the handshake lines are set to the appropriate starting levels and bit five is set high before the first read operation on the data lines. If the handshake outputs are not in use, simply write a value of 32 to the handshake output register at the start of the program and ignore this register thereafter.

A simple GW BASIC or QBASIC program is all that is needed in order to check whether or not a printer port is operating properly in the input mode. This program tests a port that has its base address at &H378, but it will obviously work with other ports if the two appropriate addresses are used.

```
10 REM BIDIRECTIONAL PORT TEST PROGRAM
20 CLS
30 OUT &H37A,32
40 LOCATE 10,30
50 PRINT INP(&H378)
60 GOTO 20
```

Line 20 clears the screen and line 30 sets the port to the input mode. Lines 40 and 50 then position the cursor towards the middle of the screen and print the value returned from the port. This routine is then repeated indefinitely, with a rapidly updated value being displayed on the screen. With most printer ports this will result in "255" being displayed on the screen, due to the use of pull-up resistors on the inputs. With other ports the inputs seem to have a high input impedance, and will be left "floating". If "255" is displayed, connecting one or two inputs to the 0-volt rail via current limiting resistors of about 330R in value should produce a reduced reading (e.g. 254 if D0 is pulled low).

If the inputs are high impedance types, simply placing a finger close to the data terminals of the port will probably be sufficient to produce changes in the reading. If no change in the reading can be produced, either the port is not a bidirectional type or it has not been set to a suitable mode. There are actually a few PCs that have built-in printer ports that support bidirectional operation, but which do not handle things in the standard manner. With a port of this type it should be possible to use it in the input mode if you can obtain the manufacturer's technical information on the PC's hardware, but using an add-on printer port card might be a better solution.

The multiplexing technique described previously can be used to increase the number of input lines available, and the circuits of Figure 3.6 and 3.7 will work well with a bidirectional printer port. However, remember to include the current limiting resistors between all the tristate buffers and the input port.

Chapter 4

SERIAL INTERFACING

Most PCs have at least one spare serial port, which makes this seem like a good way of interfacing a PC to your add-on devices. In practice using a serial port tends to be far less straightforward than interfacing an equivalent circuit to a parallel port. Where possible I would certainly recommend using a printer port or an add-on parallel port for your PC based projects. The main problem with a serial port is that it can not directly provide parallel data, or read it. A certain amount of interfacing is needed in order to accomplish the serial to parallel and parallel to serial conversions. You therefore need a fair amount of circuitry in addition to the basic hardware for your add-on.

Another point to bear in mind is that this additional circuitry only provides basic 8-bit input and 8-bit output ports with no handshake lines. There are actually handshake inputs and outputs on the serial port which can be used to control the flow of data into and out of the port, and in some circumstances it might be possible to use these as part of the handshake set-up for your add-on device. There may also be inputs and outputs available on the serial interface device that can be used as part of the handshake system for your add-on. In general though, it is best to keep any handshaking to the bare minimum. Of course, by utilizing multiplexing techniques it is possible to provide virtually any desired number of input and output lines using a serial port, but this further complicates matters. It is easy to end up with a circuit that is 90 percent serial encoding, decoding, and multiplexing and 10 percent the actual add-on device!

Another problem with a standard RS232C interface is that it is relatively slow. Using the standard transmission rates data can only be sent at about one or two kilobytes per second. This compares to rates of around 500 kilobytes per second or more for parallel interfaces. This lack of speed is not always of importance, but it does render an RS232C interface impractical for certain applications. It is usually possible to use a PC serial port at speeds beyond the normal standards, but this only speeds things up by a factor of six.

It should be pointed out that serial interfaces do have two or three advantages. Firstly, they are truly bidirectional, and all PC serial ports have the ability to both send and receive bytes of data. A serial port can also be used with long connecting cables, whereas parallel ports are normally restricted to quite short leads. In fact an ordinary PC parallel printer port should not be used with a connecting cable more than about two or three metres long. The maximum cable length for an RS232C serial port depends on the rate at which data is transferred, but cables of around 10 to 20 metres are normally satisfactory at the higher rates. In theory at any rate, cables of a kilometre or more are acceptable at the lower transfer speeds. Another advantage of serial interfacing is that only simple connecting cables are required. A basic two-way system requires just three connecting cables, and only five wires are needed if hardware handshaking is utilized. This compares to 17 wires for a basic two-way parallel system with no handshaking.

Bit-By-Bit
A serial interface sends all eight bits of data over a single line, and it must therefore send bits one at a time. This is the reason that serial interfaces tend to be relatively slow. A parallel interface transfers whole bytes at a time whereas a serial type literally transfers data on a bit-by-bit basis. A normal RS232C serial interface is asynchronous, which means that there are no additional connecting wires carrying a clock signal or some other form of synchronisation signal. The transmitting and receiving circuits must, of course, be kept correctly synchronised somehow. Synchronisation is achieved by using standard transmission rates and sending additional bits with each byte of data.

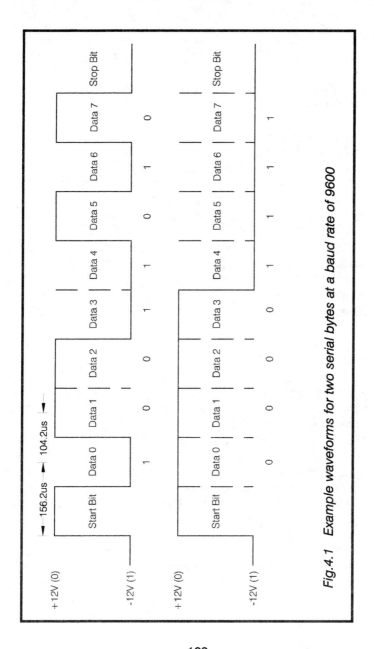

Fig.4.1 Example waveforms for two serial bytes at a baud rate of 9600

123

The two example waveforms of Figure 4.1 show how this system operates. The first point to note here is that the signal voltages are not at any form of standard 5-volt logic levels, but are instead at plus and minus 12 volts. In fact the signal voltages can be as low as 3 volts when fully loaded, but would more usually be at around 8 to 10 volts. Serial interface chips do actually operate at normal logic levels, but they interface to the RS232C connector via special line drivers and receivers. These provide level shifting so that the interface operates at the correct voltage levels, and they also provide an inversion. Hence positive and negative voltages respectively represent logic 0 and logic 1, which is the opposite of what one might expect.

RS232C serial interfaces operate at a number of standard transmission rates, or baud rates as they are known. The baud rate is simply the number of bits sent per second if there is a continuous data stream. All the standard baud rates are listed here:

| 50 | 75 | 150 | 300 | 600 |
| 1200 | 2400 | 4800 | 9600 | 19200 |

Unless you need to use very long connecting cables it is advisable to use one of the higher baud rates as these provide higher maximum transfer rates. By electronic and computing standards the maximum rate at which data can be transferred is quite low even at the higher baud rates. Including the synchronisation signals there are typically ten bits transmitted per byte, which means that baud rates of 9600 and 19200 provide maximum data transfer rates of just 960 and 1920 bytes per second. This is sufficient for many applications, but is totally inadequate for something like audio digitising. Bear in mind that there is a small delay between the commencement of data being sent and a fully decoded byte appearing at the receiving device. Using a high baud rate keeps this delay as small as possible (a little over 100 μs at 9600 baud).

The synchronisation signals are called stop and start bits, which are, as one would expect, sent immediately before and after the data bits. The start bit indicates to the receiving circuit that it must sample the signal line after a certain period of time, and this time is equal to the period of 1.5 bits. In the example of Figure 4.1 the transmission rate is 9600 baud, which works out at approximately 104.2 μs per bit (1000000 us divided by 9600 baud equals 104.2 μs). Sampling the input line after 156.2 μs (1.5 bits) therefore results in the logic level being tested in the middle of the first bit. This is always the least significant bit (D0). The input line is then tested every 104.2 μs until bits D1 through to D7 have been read into the receiver register. The data line is then returned to its standby state for 104.2 μs to produce the stop bit, which really just provides a guaranteed minimum gap from one byte of data to the next. This gives the receiving device time to deal with one byte of data before it starts to receive the next one.

Word Formats

The serial signal in this example has one start bit, eight data bits, one stop bit, and no parity checking, which is probably the most common word format. However, there are many others in use, with anything from five to eight data bits, one, one and a half, or two stop bits, and odd or even parity checking. There is always a single start bit incidentally. In the present context you will normally require eight-bit data transfers, and there is no point in using anything less than an eight bit word format. Normally it is better to use one rather than two stop bits because this gives a slightly faster maximum transfer rate, but two stop bits can be used if your add-on circuit needs a little extra time to process one byte of data before the next is received. Parity checking is a simple method of error checking that relies on an extra bit being sent at the end of bytes, where necessary, so that there is always an even or an odd number of bits. This method of checking is not very reliable since a double glitch can result in data being corrupted but the parity being left intact. It is little used in practice and I would recommend avoiding word formats that involve either type of parity checking.

Serial interfaces have a reputation for being difficult to deal with, and this is at least partially due to the numerous baud rates and word formats in use. It is not simply enough to get the transmitting and receiving devices connected together correctly. Unless both ends of the system are set up to use the same word format and baud rate it is unlikely that the system will function correctly. It will certainly fail to operate at all if the sending and receiving baud rates are different. Always make sure that both ends of the system are set to the same word format and baud rate. If a serial system fails to transfer data correctly always recheck that the transmitting and receiving circuits are set up correctly.

UART

It is probably not that difficult to decode a serial signal using a circuit based on a shift register, but there are numerous devices available that provide the necessary decoding and control hardware. Many of these devices are designed to operate on the bus of a microprocessor and are not really suitable for operation in most PC add-ons. For serial interfacing to a non-microprocessor-based add-on it is a UART (universal asynchronous receiver/transmitter) that is required. The industry standard UART is the 6402, which can handle any standard word format and baud rate.

This is a 40-pin device which has the pinout configuration shown in Figure 4.2. As the UART name suggests, both serial-to-parallel and parallel-to-serial conversion are catered for. The device has tristate outputs that can be directly interfaced to the busses of many microprocessors, as can its inputs. It works equally well in normal logic circuits with the outputs permanently enabled and the inputs either hard-wired or controlled via standard logic circuits. The important point here is that it does not require a microprocessor and a software routine in order to

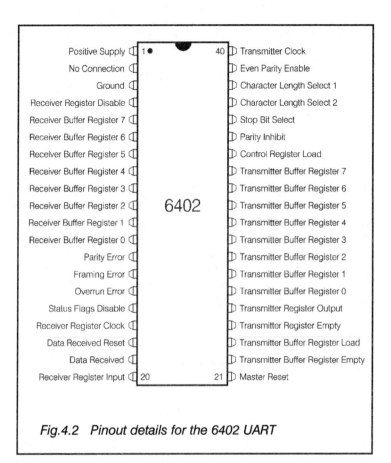

Positive Supply	1●	40	Transmitter Clock
No Connection			Even Parity Enable
Ground			Character Length Select 1
Receiver Register Disable			Character Length Select 2
Receiver Buffer Register 7			Stop Bit Select
Receiver Buffer Register 6			Parity Inhibit
Receiver Buffer Register 5			Control Register Load
Receiver Buffer Register 4			Transmitter Buffer Register 7
Receiver Buffer Register 3			Transmitter Buffer Register 6
Receiver Buffer Register 2	6402		Transmitter Buffer Register 5
Receiver Buffer Register 1			Transmitter Buffer Register 4
Receiver Buffer Register 0			Transmitter Buffer Register 3
Parity Error			Transmitter Buffer Register 2
Framing Error			Transmitter Buffer Register 1
Overrun Error			Transmitter Buffer Register 0
Status Flags Disable			Transmitter Register Output
Receiver Register Clock			Transmitter Register Empty
Data Received Reset			Transmitter Buffer Register Load
Data Received			Transmitter Buffer Register Empty
Receiver Register Input	20	21	Master Reset

Fig.4.2   Pinout details for the 6402 UART

set the required word format. Simply connecting a few inputs to the correct logic levels is all that is needed in order to perform this task.

Pins 34 to 39 control the word format, and pin 34 is the control register load input. A high level on pin 34 loads the control register and it can simply be wired permanently to logic one if the other control inputs are to be hard-wired. The functions of the other control pins are as shown overleaf.

Pin 35, Parity Inhibit
A high level on this input inhibits parity generation during transmission, and switches off parity checking during reception.

PIN 36, Stop Bit Select
Setting this input high selects two stop bits (1.5 for five data bit formats). With this input set low the word format has one stop bit.

Pins 37 and 38, Character Length Select 1/2
These two inputs select the word length (the number of data bits) as per this table;

Word Length	CLS1	CLS2
5-bits	Low	Low
6-bits	High	Low
7-bits	Low	High
8-bits	High	High

Pin 39, Even Parity Enable
This input is set high for even parity or low for odd parity. Note that this input has no effect if pin 35 (parity inhibit) is set high and parity is disabled.

The word control inputs are common to both the transmitter and receiver sections of the 6402, but there are separate clock inputs. The transmitter clock input is at pin 40 and the receiver clock input is at pin 17. In both cases the clock frequency must be sixteen times the required baud rate and must not exceed 3.2 MHz. This enables baud rates of up to 200000 (200 kilobaud) to be accommodated, which is far more than adequate for normal requirements. Even if you set a PC serial port to operate at a higher than normal rate a 6402 UART should be able to cope.

Pin 21 is the master reset input, and this must be supplied with a positive pulse at switch-on in order to ensure that the chip initialises correctly. In comparison to most chips a fairly long reset pulse is needed, but a simple C - R network is still sufficient. The positive and 0-volt supplies connect to pins one and three respectively. The 6402 will actually operate over a supply voltage range of 4 to 10 volts (4 to 6.5 volts for the 6402C), but it will normally be operated from a standard 5-volt supply. It is based on CMOS technology and the supply current therefore depends on the clock frequency, but the supply current is usually less than two milliamps.

Receiver

The input data, which must be at normal 5-volt logic levels, is fed to the receiver register input at pin 20. Decoded bytes appear on the eight receiver buffer register outputs at pins 5 (most significant) to 12 (least significant). These are tristate inputs that are controlled by the receiver register disable input (pin 4). The outputs go to the high impedance state when pin 4 is taken high. This facility is not usually needed and pin 4 is then connected to ground so that the receiver outputs are permanently enabled.

When a new byte of data is received the data received flag at pin 19 goes high. A low pulse applied to the data received reset input at pin 18 can be used to reset this flag. In many applications these inputs are not needed, because the main add-on circuit will automatically respond to new bytes of data as and when they are received. For example, feeding fresh data to a digital-to-analogue converter results in it altering its output to suit without the need for any control signals such as a strobe pulse. Not all circuits are so accommodating though, and in some cases a signal is needed to indicate that fresh data is available. As an example, in some applications data might be sent in (say) groups of three bytes, and the receiving circuit then needs some means of counting in the bytes so that it knows which byte is which, and when all three have been received. This requires a strobe pulse each time a fresh byte has been received. Using the data received flag to reset itself can produce this signal. All that is needed is an inverter and a short delay circuit between the data received flag and the data received reset input. A strobe pulse is then generated each time a fresh byte of data is placed on the outputs.

There are three error flags available at pins 13 to 15, and these respectively indicate a parity error, a framing error (an incorrect stop bit or first stop bit), and an overrun error. The latter occurs when a new byte of data is fully decoded before the data received flag has been reset. These outputs can be used to operate warning LEDs or something of this nature, but in most cases you will be all too aware if something goes wrong with the decoding process, rendering the warning LEDs of little practical use.

Transmitter

On the transmitter side of things the eight bits of parallel data are supplied to the transmitter buffer register inputs at pins 26 (least significant) to 33 (most significant). In order to transmit the data the transmitter buffer register load input at pin 23 must be pulsed low. As with most serial devices, a system of buffering is utilized, with the data being transferred to the buffer register on the high to low transition, and then into the transmitter register on the low to high transition. If the transmitter register is full the second transfer is delayed until it is empty. This still leaves the possibility of overwriting a byte of data in the transmitter buffer register. One way of avoiding this is to use a timing circuit to ensure that data can not be written to the interface at an excessive rate. Another is to use the two handshake outputs available on the 6402. These are the transmitter buffer register empty (pin 22) and the transmitter register empty (pin 24) flags, both of which go high when their respective registers are empty. These flags, and those of the receiver section, are tristate types. They are all set to the high impedance state by taking the status flag disable input (pin 16) high, or enabled by taking this input low. The serial data stream is provided on the transmitter register output at pin 25, and this operates at normal 5-volt logic levels.

Receiver Circuit

Figure 4.3 shows the circuit diagram for a simple serial-to-parallel converter based on the 6402 UART. The crystal oscillator based on TR1 generates the clock signal, and this operates at 2.4576 MHz. The baud rate provided by the UART is one sixteenth of this frequency, which works out at a baud rate of 153600 baud. A baud rate of 9600 is needed, which requires the 2.4576 MHz signal to be divided by sixteen again. This division is provided by the first four stages of IC1, which is a CMOS 4024BE seven stage binary counter. Using other outputs of IC1 can provide these additional baud rates.

Output (pin no.)	Baud Rate
Q3 (9)	19200
Q5 (5)	4800
Q6 (4)	2400
Q7 (3)	1200

Special line receivers are available, but unless long connecting cables are used a simple transistor inverter stage is all that is needed to provide the inversion and level shifting at the serial input. This is the function of TR2. C4 and R6 provide the reset pulse to the UART (IC2) at switch-on. The control register inputs are hard wired for a word format of eight data bits, one stop bit, and no parity checking, but you can obviously change the wiring to produce any required format. However, this word format is the most common one these days, and there is no point in using a different one unless you really do need a different word format for some reason.

The decoded bytes of data are produced on outputs D0 to D7, and are at 5-volt CMOS logic levels. In practice they also seem to drive 74LS** logic devices properly, but would probably have insufficient drive currents to drive standard TTL devices (which are now obsolete anyway). TR3 inverts the output signal from the data received flag and uses it to reset this flag by way of the data received reset input. This produces an output pulse

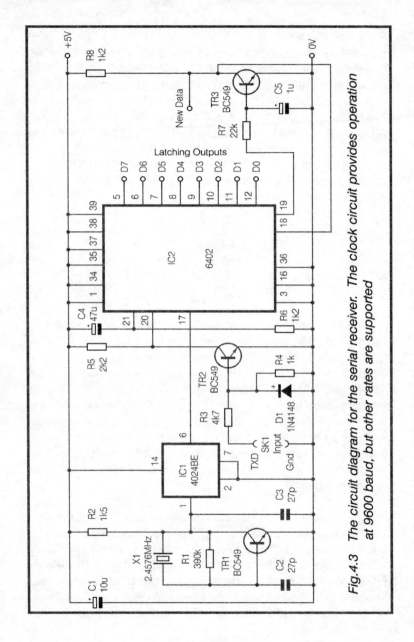

Fig.4.3 The circuit diagram for the serial receiver. The clock circuit provides operation at 9600 baud, but other rates are supported

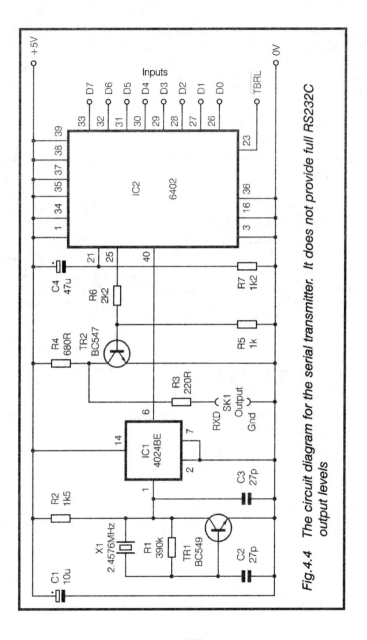

Fig.4.4 The circuit diagram for the serial transmitter. It does not provide full RS232C output levels

133

each time fresh data appears on the outputs. C5 stretches the low output pulse that is produced at the collector of TR3. This stretching will not always be required, and if continuous streams of data are used it might be necessary to reduce the value of C5 to around 47n.

Transmitter Circuit

Figure 4.4 shows the circuit diagram for the parallel to serial converter. The clock circuit is identical to the one used in the receiver circuit, and in a transmitter/receiver circuit it is perfectly all right to use the same clock circuit for both sections of the unit provided they are to operate at the same baud rate. C4 and R7 provide the reset pulse at switch-on, and in a transmitter receiver circuit these will be common to both sections of the unit, as will IC2 itself. The control inputs of IC2 are programmed to produce a word format of eight data bits, one stop bit and no parity checking. They can be reconfigured to produce other formats, but remember that in a two-way system the reception and transmission word formats have to be the same.

The line driver consists of a simple transistor inverter stage based on TR2. This does not provide proper RS232C signal voltages, which require minimum loaded drive potentials of plus and minus 3 volts. This circuit provides drive voltages of 0 and +5 volts. In practice the lack of a true negative output level does not normally stop an RS232C interface from working, and it avoids the need for plus and minus 12-volt supplies. However, proper operation without the correct drive potentials can not be guaranteed, and it is unlikely to work when using long connecting cables. It is certainly worth trying though, as it greatly simplifies things in circumstances where it will work. If your application requires a proper line driver, refer to the section of this chapter that deals with line driver and receiver devices.

In order to transmit a byte of data the TBRL input of IC2 must be pulsed low, and this function must be provided by some control logic in the main add-on circuit. For reliable operation the data on the input lines must be stable immediately prior to and during the pulse on TBRL. This pulse can be quite short, but it is probably best to err on the side of caution and use a pulse that is about one UART clock cycle in length. The transmitter register is loaded on the rising edge at the end of the pulse, and transmission then commences.

It is important that data is not written to the serial interface at an excessive rate. In many applications this will not be a problem, with only the odd byte of data be sent to the interface here and there. The real problem occurs where bursts of data will be handled by the interface, even if each data burst only consists of three or four bytes. There are two ways of handling the problem, and one of these is to design the control logic of the main circuit to regulate the flow of data, and prevent bytes from being sent at an excessive rate. Where this approach can be implemented reasonably easily it will almost certainly represent the best approach to the problem. The other method is to use one of the handshake outputs of the UART to provide a hold-off so that data can not be sent to the interface at a rate it can not handle. It will probably not matter whether the TRE (pin 24) or TBRE (pin 22) output is used. In either case data should not be written to the interface unless the handshake output is high.

Connections

The normal connector for an RS232C interface is a 25-pin D type, but many PCs have the AT style 9-pin connector. In both cases the connector on the computer is a male connector, and you require a female type to make the connections to the port. Figure 4.5 provides connection details for both types of PC serial port. Where possible, which in practice is actually the vast majority of cases, no form of handshaking should be used. A serial interface is slow by normal computing standards, and very slow by general electronic standards. Consequently, when sending data to an add-on via a serial interface the add-on should be able to handle a continuous flow of data. Similarly, even an old PC with a relatively slow processor should be able to process

135

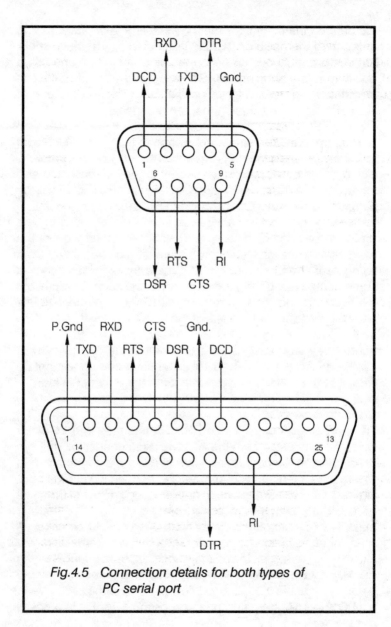

Fig.4.5   Connection details for both types of
PC serial port

136

a continuous flow of data without difficulty. With no handshaking used the interconnections are very simple, and it is just a matter of the two input or output leads of the interface to the corresponding terminals of the PC's RS232C port.

There is a possible complication in that some PCs are reluctant to send data unless the handshake inputs are held at the level that indicates the receiving device is ready for action. For some reason this may even "gum up the works" when the PC is set to use software handshaking or no handshaking at all. The root of the problem is that handshake inputs may assume the hold-off state if they are simply left floating. A simple solution that usually works is to cross-couple the serial port's handshake lines. In practice this means connecting the clear to send (CTS) and data set ready (DSR) inputs to the request to send (RTS) and data terminal ready (DTR) outputs respectively. If that fails to free things up, try connecting the ring indicator input to one of the handshake outputs as well.

On the face of it there is no reason for having two sets of handshake lines, since one set is all that is needed to control the flow of data. The usual scheme of things, if both sets are actually operational, is to have CTS and RTS to control the flow of data, with DTR and DSR indicating whether or not the receiving device is actually operational. If a serial printer is off-line because it is out of paper for example, this would be indicated via DTR and DSR. The CTS and RTS lines would be used to control the flow of data when the printer was on-line. In reality the way in which the handshake lines are used varies somewhat from one serial device to another, and serial links will sometimes only function if they are connected in what is theoretically the wrong manner. It is mainly for this reason that hardware handshaking is best avoided where possible. Where it is implemented it often results in a try everything until it works approach.

You may come across references to software handshaking, or XON/XOFF handshaking, as it is also known. This is where the handshaking is controlled via software codes sent from the receiving device to the transmitting device via a data link. With this type of handshaking you therefore need a full-duplex (two-way) link even though data is only being sent in one direction (half-duplex operation). The ASCII codes 17 and 19 are normally used for XON (switch on) and XOFF (switch off) respectively. In theory it is not necessary to have the handshake lines coupled together, but in practice the sending device may refuse to send anything unless its handshake inputs are at the "on" voltage. Presumably it decides that the receiving device is off-line and refuses to start transmitting until it gets the appropriate input level on one or both of its handshake inputs. It would obviously be possible to use this type of handshaking with your own projects, but it would seem to be doing things the hard way. Also, this method is not noted for its reliability, so if handshaking is deemed absolutely necessary it is best to adopt the hardware method.

You might also encounter references to DCE and DTE when dealing with serial interfacing. These respectively stand for data communications equipment and data terminal equipment. In theory a serial link normally consists of a DCE device and a DTE type. A computer is normally the device that controls the system, and would be a DTE unit. Something like a printer or one of your add-ons would normally be the controlled device, or the DCE unit in serial interfacing terminology. The difference between the two types is that DTE units transmit on their "TXD" outputs and receive on their "RXD" inputs. Things are done the other way round with DCE units, which transmit on their "RXD" lines and receive on their "TXD" lines. The handshake lines are also swapped over so that inputs become outputs and vice versa. This may seem to be pointless and potentially confusing, and I suppose that a good case to this effect could be made. Apparently the reason for having the two categories of equipment is that it enables a so-called "straight" connecting cable to be used. In other words, the cable connects pin 1 at one end to pin 1 at the other, pin two to pin two, and so on. Connecting two DCE units together, or two DTE types, requires the correct method of cross coupling for successful operation. For example, pin two at one end has to connect to pin three at the other in order to provide a data link.

When you are constructing your own serial units there should be no confusion about the method of connection. A PC is a DTE device, and it does things in the logical way with data output from "TXD" and received on "RXD". In the circuits of Figures 4.2 and 4.3 the labelling on the input and output sockets shows the terminals of the PC serial ports that the lines connect to incidentally.

Line Drivers/Receivers
As pointed out previously, it is often possible to use simple inverters rather than proper RS232C line drivers and receivers. However, if you are using long connecting cables it is best to opt for the real thing, and clearly it is also necessary to fit proper line drivers to your projects when faced with a PC that will not work reliably with reduced drive voltages. The standard line drivers and receivers are the MC1488P and MC1489P respectively. These are both quad devices, but any unwanted sections can simply be left unused. Pinout details for both devices are provided in Figure 4.6.

Three of the line drivers in the MC1488P have two inputs, and effectively operate as NAND gates having outputs at line voltages. In most applications the gate capability is not required and either the two inputs of each driver must be driven in parallel, or the unused input must be tied high. The line receivers of the MC1489P each have a control input that can be used to alter the input threshold level, and it also has possible application in counteracting certain types of noise. In most cases though the control inputs are left unused.

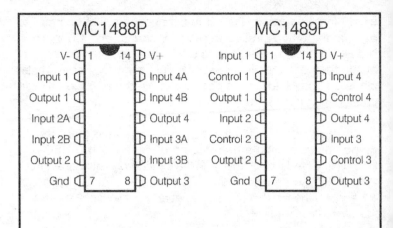

Fig.4.6 Pinout details for the MC1488P and MC1489P line driver and receiver chips

One slight problem with the MC1489P is that it requires dual balanced 12-volt supplies in order to provide the correct output potentials. It would often be more convenient if a single 5-volt positive supply could be used. One solution to the problem is to use a switch mode power supply circuit to produce dual balanced 12-volt rails from a 5-volt supply. An alternative is to use a device such as the MAX202, which is effectively a standard dual line driver plus a built-in switch mode power supply circuit. This enables it to produce adequate output potentials from a standard 5-volt logic supply. As an added bonus the MAX202 also includes a couple of line receivers. The circuit diagram for a dual line driver/receiver based on the MAX202 appears in Figure 4.7. The switch mode power supply is a simple capacitive pump type, and no inductors are required. The five capacitors must be high quality types suitable for use in switching circuits, and tantalum capacitors are probably the best choice.

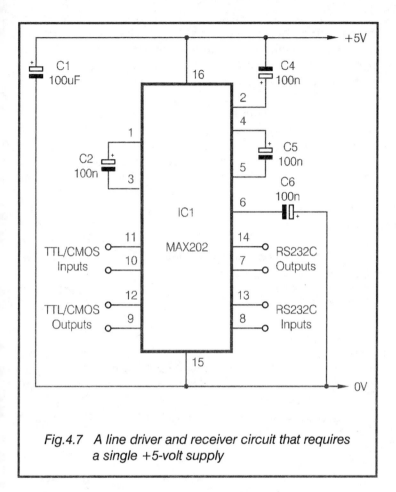

Fig.4.7   A line driver and receiver circuit that requires a single +5-volt supply

Making Contact

Any high level language should have built-in support for the PC's serial ports. Unfortunately, this support is usually slanted towards the sending and receiving of files rather than byte-by-byte operation. You can, of course, send a one-byte file to a serial port, but there will probably be another byte or bytes sent with the data byte, such as an end of file marker. The hardware in your add-on has to be designed to take this sort of thing into account. Similarly, when sending serial data to a PC's serial port it may be necessary to include additional bytes to help the software digest the data properly.

Where the programming language you are using supports direct port access you can try controlling the serial port hardware directly. This is not too difficult when sending data, where it is basically just a matter of writing the data to the appropriate input/output address. A timing loop can be used to ensure that data is not written to the port at an excessive rate, or you could try reading the appropriate status flag of the chip. Reading data direct from a serial port is much trickier, since the operating system will be dealing with bytes of data as and when they arrive. This is almost invariably achieved via interrupt routines. You must not use software routines that compete with the operating system. Unless you really know what you are doing, direct reading of the serial port is not a practical proposition.

The serial ports are written to and read at the base address of the port. These are the four serial port base addresses, but note that under certain circumstances the operating system might shuffle the ports into a slightly different scheme of things (ports two and four having their address ranges swapped over for example). This table also shows the IRQ numbers for each port.

Port	Base Address	IRQ
One	3F8	4
Two	2F8	3
Three	3E8	4
Four	2E8	3

Direct control of a serial port, other than the data register, can be a slightly "hit and miss" affair as there have been several serial interface chips used in PCs over the years. However, they are to a large extent compatible, and you are unlikely to encounter major problems to due to a lack of chip compatibility. The original PCs used an 8250 chip, but most recent PCs have used the 16550, or a variant of this device. In fact modern PCs have a single chip to handle the basic input/output functions, and this chip includes a section that is functionally the same as a device from the 16550 family. Anyway, this is the "standard" scheme of things for the serial port registers.

Address	R/W	Register	DLAB
Base	Read	Received Data	0
Base	Write	Data To Transmit	0
Base	R/W	Clock Divider Latch (LSB)	1
Base + 1	R/W	Clock Divider Latch (MSB)	1
Base + 1	Write	Interrupt Enable Register	0
Base + 2	Read	Interrupt Identification Register	
Base + 3	R/W	Line Control Register	
Base + 4	R/W	Modem Control Register	
Base + 5	Read	Line Status Register	
Base + 6	Read	Modem Status Register	
Base + 7	-	Reserved	

There is a slight complication in that two registers have different functions depending on the setting of the divisor latch access bit (DLAB), which is bit seven of the line control register. This bit must be set to 0 to gain access to the data registers and the interrupt enable register, and to 1 to access the two clock divider latches.

It can be useful to control the divider latches directly as they permit the baud rate to be controlled. The clock for the serial chip is at a frequency of 1.8432 MHz, but there is an internal division by 16 so that the baud rate is one sixteenth of this figure (115.2 kilobaud). Placing a divisor into the clock divider latches, which together hold a 16-bit value, can reduce the baud rate further. This gives a division range of 1 to 65535. The baud rate of a serial port can usually be set via the operating system, and can be set using the built-in facilities of some programming languages. However, direct control offers a simple but effective alternative. It also enables the use of any baud rate supported by the hardware, rather than restricting you to the standard rates. Using a value of zero for the MSB and one for the LSB provides a baud rate of 115.2 kilobaud, and permits substantially faster data transfers than the highest standard rate of 19.2 kilobaud. Data can be transferred at over 11k per second using this rate. This is still quite slow by parallel port standards, but it is more than adequate for most applications. It has to be pointed out that not all PC serial ports are guaranteed to work at 115.2 kilobaud, but the serial ports of any reasonably modern PC should be able to do so.

Interrupts
The interrupt enable register is reasonably straightforward, and the functions of each bit are detailed in this table:

Bit	Function
0	Received Data Available
1	Transmitter Holding Register Empty
2	Receiver Line Status
3	Modem Status
4	Enables Sleep Mode (only if 16750 UART fitted)
5	Enables Low Power Mode (only if 16750 UART fitted)
6	Reserved
7	Reserved

In each case setting a bit high enables that form of interrupt. With bit 0 set high an interrupt is generated when the receiving register has a fresh byte of data available. The easiest way of directly reading the port is probably to disable this interrupt and use polling instead. Polling simply means frequent testing of the appropriate status flag, with the port being read when it indicates fresh data is available. This method is less efficient in that it involves more work for the processor, but with the received data interrupt disabled it should avoid conflicts with the operating system. Bit 1 produces an interrupt when the transmitter register is empty and the chip is ready to receive a new byte of data for transmission. Again, it is probably easiest to disable this interrupt and rely on polling or timing loops to prevent data being written to the port at an excessive rate. Bits 2 and 3 enable receiver line status and modem status interrupts, which you will probably not need to implement.

When bit 0 of the interrupt identification register is at 0 an interrupt is pending, and bits 1 and 2 identify the pending interrupt with the highest priority in this fashion:

Bit 2	Bit 1	Priority	Source
0	0	Fourth	Modem Status
0	1	Third	Transmitter Register
1	0	Second	Receiver Data
1	1	First	Receiver Line Status

Word Control
The line control register controls the word format for reception and transmission. This is a summary of the bit functions:

Bits 0 and 1
These set the number of data bits as follows:

Bit 0	Bit 1	Word Length
0	0	5
0	1	6
1	0	7
1	1	8

Bit 2
This bit is set low for one stop bit or high for two stop bits (1.5 stop bits for five data bit operation)

Bit 3

The parity enable bit. Set to 1 to enable parity or 0 to disable parity checking.

Bit 4

This bit selects the type of parity checking used, but obviously has no effect if parity is disabled via bit 3. Set this bit to 1 for even parity or 0 for odd parity.

Bit 5

The stuck parity bit.

Bit 6

The set break control bit. Set to 0 for normal operation, or to 1 to force the serial output pin of the chip to logic 0.

Bit 7

Divisor Latch Access Bit (DLAB).

Modem Control Register

The modem control register is used primarily to control the data terminal ready (bit 0) and request to send (bit 1) handshake outputs. In both cases logic 0 sets the output to the standby state and logic 1 sets it to the active state. Bit 4 provides a loopback feature for diagnostic testing.

Line Status Register

The line status register enables various status flags to be read. This is a summary of the bit functions:

Bit 0

This is the received data ready flag, and it is set high when a complete character has been received and transferred to the receiver buffer register. Writing a 0 to it can reset this bit, but it is reset automatically when the received data is read.

Bit 1

This is the overrun flag, and it is set to 1 when a byte of data is placed in the receiver buffer register before the previous byte was read. It is reset when the line status register is read.

Bit 2

Bit 2 is set to 1 when a parity error is detected. It is reset when the line status register is read.

Bit 3

The framing error bit. When it is set to 1 the last character received did not have a valid stop bit.

Bit 4

This is the break interrupt indicator. It is set at 1 when the received data input is held at logic 0 for more than the duration of one complete character including start and stop bits, etc.

Bits 0 to 4 are all error flags, and any of these being activated causes a line status interrupt to be generated.

Bit 5

The transmitter holding register empty bit. This flag is set to 0 when the processor loads the transmitter holding register and to 1 when a character is transferred from the holding register to the transmitter register. In other words, when set to 1 it indicates that the transmitter holding register is ready to receive another byte of data. It also generates an interrupt request.

Bit 6

This is the transmitter empty indicator. It is set to 1 whenever the transmitter holding register and the transmitter shift register are both empty. It is at 0 whenever either register contains a byte of data.

Bit 7

Unused and always at logic 0.

Modem Status Register

The modem status register enables handshake and other inputs to be read. The bit functions are as follows:

Bit 0
This is the delta clear to send input. When set to 1 it indicates that the clear to send input has changed state since it was last read.

Bit 1
Similar to Bit 0, but for the data set ready handshake input.

Bit 2
The trailing edge ring indicator detector. It indicates that the ring indicator input has changed from the active state to the inactive state.

Bit 3
This bit indicates that the data carrier detect input of the serial chip has changed state.

Note that bits 0 to 3 generate a modem status interrupt when they are set to 1.

Bit 4
Reads clear to send line.

Bit 5
Reads data set ready line.

Bit 6
Reads ring indicator line.

Bit 7
Reads data carrier detect line.

An easy way to start experimenting with direct control of a serial port is to first set the divisor latch access bit to 1 by writing a value of 128 (decimal) to the line control register. This gives access to the divisor latches so that you can set the required baud rate. Use values of 0 and 12 (decimal) for the most and least significant bytes respectively, which gives a baud rate of 9600. Set the registers back to normal operation by writing a value of 0 to the line control register. Bytes for transmission are then written to the transmitter register at the base address, but where necessary use a timing loop to prevent bytes from being transmitted at more than one byte per millisecond. Alternatively, use a loop to monitor bit 5 of the line status register. A new byte of data should only be written to the serial port when this bit is at logic 1.

Received data is read from the base address of the port, but this address should only be read when fresh data is available. Whether or not new data is available can be determined by monitoring bit 0 of the line status register. This bit goes to logic 1 when a fresh byte is available, and therefore data should only be read when this bit is at 1. It is automatically reset when the received data register is read. Initially it is probably best not to use interrupts, and to disable interrupts generated by the port so that there are no conflicts with the operating system. This is achieved by writing a value of zero to the interrupt enable register.

Chapter 5

SOFTWARE CONSIDERATIONS

Users of high level programming languages are often largely insulated from the fact that computers operate in binary, and that all the data they handle is reduced to a series of 1 and 0s. The software and computer hardware accepts text characters from the keyboard and produces text output on the screen. The situation is very different for those dealing with add-on projects, which usually require control on a bit-by-bit basis. It is possible to design (say) a computer robot that understands the text string "turn left", but most do-it-yourself add-ons are not this sophisticated. The robot is more likely to require something like the binary code 00001111 (0F in hexadecimal). In this chapter we will take a look at the binary and hexadecimal numbering systems, bitwise operations, and how to contact your projects with a high-level programming language.

Applied Logic
Some applications are well suited to digital control and it does not take much imagination to see how logic circuits can be put to use in these. As an example, suppose that a circuit must control a row of lights and produce a moving-lights display. Each light is either on or off, and this type of control obviously suits the logic way of doing things with just two signal levels. Each light can be switched on by a logic 1 level and switched off by a logic 0 level. It is just a matter of producing a circuit that will produce the right sequence of 0s and 1s at its outputs, and keep repeating this sequence at the required rate.

Most "real world" applications do not require straightforward on/off switching, but instead deal with quantities of something. For example, a weighing scale does not operate on the basis of something being heavy or not, but deals in actual weights. Digital systems can handle quantities quite easily, and it is just a matter of using a number of digital lines, together with a suitable method of coding. Letters of the alphabet, punctuation marks, etc., are usually represented by ASCII codes, and these use seven lines to carry the codes. Each set of seven 1s and 0s represents a different character. For instance, the code 1010101 represents the upper-case letter "U".

A digital circuit can represent numeric values of any magnitude, but it requires a large number of digits to represent quite modest values. Even so, with the current technology this still represents by far the easiest way of using electronic circuits to handle numbers. Although the mathematics are being handled in what could be regarded as a rather clumsy fashion, the speed of electronic circuits is such that number-crunching is carried out at very high speeds. Also, as already pointed out, the fact that a digital system is operating using 1s and 0s is not normally apparent to the user. Representing a single quantity using logic signals is clearly quite easy, but how does a digital system handle something like an audio signal that is constantly changing? A digital system can handle varying quantities using a system known as sampling. Although this word is now synonymous with digital audio recording, it is in fact a general term that is applicable to any digital system that deals with what is essentially analogue data. It basically just entails taking a series of readings so that the system tracks the rises and falls in the amplitude of the audio signal, temperature, or whatever.

Strictly speaking, a digital system can not fully accommodate analogue signals since it can never have infinite resolution. With analogue signals that are constantly varying, the input signal is converted into a series of fixed values. No matter how frequently samples are taken, there will always be a jump from one sample value to the next. However, provided the resolution of the system is good enough, and samples are taken at a high enough rates, for all practical purposes a digital system will be as good as an analogue equivalent. The jumps in level from one sample to the next will be of no consequence. In fact, in many areas of electronics it is now true to say that the best digital systems outperform the best analogue types. Whether a digital system is dealing with individual pieces of data, or a series of samples, the resolution is crucial. In other words, is the jump from one level to the next small enough to enable any value to be depicted with good accuracy? The minimum acceptable resolution varies considerably from one application to another.

Bits and Bytes
The numbering system we use in everyday life is, of course, the decimal system, or "denary" system as it is alternatively known. This method of numbering is based on the number 10, but it is quite possible to have a system based on any number. There is normally no point in doing so, and the old imperial measures, which were based on a variety of numbers (12 in the case of feet and inches for example), have now been largely phased-out in favour of the metric system.

I suppose that binary could reasonably be regarded as the simplest possible method of numbering. It is based on the number two. In the decimal numbering system the single digit numbers are from 0 to 9, but in binary they are only from 0 to 1. In other words, the only valid numbers for each digit are 0 and 1, and absolutely nothing else is allowed! As already pointed out, representing just two numbers by an electrical signal is very easy. A low voltage is used to represent a 0, and a higher voltage represents a 1. In the case of ports and other external signals these levels are often called "low" and "high" respectively, but these terms are not usually applied to internal signals of a processor. When dealing with internal signals the alternatives of clear (logic 0) and set (logic 1) are often encountered.

Although convenient for the hardware producers, this simple logic system has its limitations and drawbacks. There have been suggestions over the years that circuits which can work directly in decimal will be a practical proposition for widespread use before too long, but there seems to be little real prospect of such a development in the near future. For the time being circuits that work in binary are the only practical ones for general use.

Binary is easier to understand if you first analyse what an ordinary decimal number represents. If we consider the decimal number 238 for instance, the eight represents eight units (10 to the power of 0), the 3 represents three tens (10 to the power of 1), and the 2 represents two hundreds (10 to the power of 2). Things are similar with a binary number such as 1101. Working from right to left again, the columns of numbers respectively represent the units (2 to the power of 0), the 2s (2 to the power of 1), the 4s (2 to the power of 2), the 8s (2 to the power of 3), and so on. 1101 in binary is therefore equivalent to 13 in decimal $(1 + 0 + 4 + 8 = 13)$.

It takes a lot of binary digits to represent numbers of quite modest magnitude, but this is the price that has to be paid for the convenience of simple binary hardware. A binary digit is normally contracted to the term "bit". One bit on its own is of limited value, and bits are normally used in groups of eight, or multiples of eight. A group of eight bits is normally termed a "byte". A byte can only handle numbers from 0 to 255 (decimal). This is adequate for some purposes, but it is often necessary to handle larger values. A 16 bit binary number is usually termed a "word", and this gives a range of 0 to 65535 (decimal). 32 bits gives a range of 0 to something over four thousand million, which should be adequate for most purposes. A 32-bit number is sometimes termed a "long word". Modern PCs use 16 or (more usually these days) 32-bit processors, but you will normally do things 8 bits at a time when dealing with user add-ons.

This table shows the number represented by bits in 16 bit numbers, and this might help to clarify the way in which the binary system operates. The numbers in the table are the ones that the bits represent when a 1 is present in that column of the binary number. If there is a 0 in a column, then that column always contributes 0 to the value of the number. We are using the convention of calling the units column bit 0, running through to bit 15 for the left-most column (not bits 1 to 16). The units column is often called the "least significant bit", or "LSB" for short. Bit 31 (or the left-most column that is actually used) is termed the "most significant bit", or just "MSB".

Bit	Dec. Value	Bit	Dec. Value
0	1	8	256
1	2	9	512
2	4	10	1024
3	8	11	2048
4	16	12	4096
5	32	13	8192
6	64	14	16384
7	128	15	32768

Signed Binary

The binary system described so far, which is often called "direct binary", is inadequate for many practical purposes. It is certainly all that is needed when designing PC based projects, but it is not sufficient for all purposes. The main drawback of direct binary is that it can not handle negative numbers. Obviously you can simply add a minus sign ahead of a binary number to indicate that it is a negative number, but you have to bear in mind that for computer applications this is not valid. There is logic 0 and logic 1, but no logic – level!

The normal way around the problem is to use "signed binary". With a signed binary number the first bit is used to denote whether the number is positive or negative. The convention is for the first bit to be a 0 for positive numbers and a 1 for negative numbers. With this system the normal 8 bit range of 0 to 255 is replaced with a range of –127 to +127 (11111111 to 01111111). The problem is solved at the expense of decreased maximum magnitude for a given number of bits. Note though, that where two or more bytes (or words or long words) are used together to form a large number, only the most significant bit of the most significant byte needs to be used to indicate the sign of the number. It is not necessary to sacrifice the most significant bit of each byte to this task.

Obviously a certain amount of care needs to be exercised when dealing with binary numbers, and you must know whether you are dealing with direct or signed binary numbers. For instance, 10000001 could be 129 (direct binary) or –1 (signed binary). I have encountered computers which have a binary to decimal conversion facility, and which seem to get confused in this way. Results were as expected for answers up to 32767, but things went completely wrong with higher numbers. This happens where the computer operates with binary numbers of up to 16 bits in length, and it interprets any values that it is fed as signed binary. This works fine if you know that it is working with signed binary. It also works fine if it is fed with binary values of 15 bits in length or less. The leading zeros then inform the computer that the number is a positive one, and the right answer is obtained. For numbers of more than 32767 the most significant bit is a 1, telling the computer that it is a negative number, even if you require a direct binary conversion.

In this basic form the signed binary system has its limitations. The problem is that although it can represent a wide range of positive and negative values perfectly adequately, calculations on simple signed binary numbers do not give the correct result. This is of only academic importance to users of high-level applications programs and applications software. You give the computer such numeric data, positive, negative, or a mixture of the two, and everything is sorted out for you. It is something that is of greater importance to the low-level (assembly language or machine code) programmer, but here we will only consider the high-level approach.

Binary Coded Decimal

Several microprocessors can operate using another form of binary called "binary coded decimal", or just "BCD", and some computer add-ons require signals in this form. BCD uses four binary bits (often termed a "nibble") to represent each decimal digit. The system operates in the manner shown below.

Decimal Number	Binary Code
0	0000
1	0001
2	0010
3	0011
4	0100
5	0101
6	0110
7	0111
8	1000
9	1001

The binary number is in fact just the ordinary binary bit code for the number concerned, and it is only for numbers of more than 9 that the system is different. The binary codes from 1010 to 1111 are unused, and all two-digit decimal numbers require 8 bit BCD codes. For instance, the decimal number 64 would be represented by the 8-bit BCD code 01100100. The first four bits (0110) represent the six, and the second four bits (0100) represent the four. Each byte can therefore represent any two digit decimal number from 0 to 99, which compares to a range of 0 to 255 for an ordinary 8 bit binary number. This helps to contribute to the relative inefficiency of the BCD system. Of course, when a nibble is incremented by 1 from a value of 1001 (9 in decimal) it does not go to 1010 (which is an illegal code in BCD), but cycles back to 0000. A carry forward of 1 should then be taken to the next BCD nibble. Since the PCs do not operate directly in BCD, you must provide the conversion from direct binary to BCD using suitable software routines. Look-up tables are the normal method for handling this type of thing.

With BCD there is no difficulty in handling large numbers, and it is just a matter of using several bytes in order to accommodate the required number of digits. Negative numbers and decimal points can also be handled with ease by this system, but this requires several additional bits. This information is usually carried in the most significant bits (i.e. the left-hand end of the number), but you can design the software and hardware to handle this type of thing in any way that you see fit. Provided the software and hardware are designed to use the same system everything should work fine.

Hexadecimal

The hexadecimal numbering system is much used in computing. The hexadecimal name is usually abbreviated to just "hex". A problem with binary numbers is that they tend to have many digits with each one being a 0 or a 1, which makes them rather difficult to deal with in many circumstances. For instance, dealing with 10 or 12 bit addresses in their binary form would probably be beyond most people's ability, as would dealing with eight-bit data values. On the other hand, binary numbers give a graphic representation of each bit in the register of a microprocessor, control register of a peripheral chip, output terminals of a printer port, or whatever. This is something that is often important, but is especially so when dealing with a microprocessor and its ports. Decimal numbers are much easier to deal with in that they are much shorter and are in a more familiar form. Unfortunately, a decimal number does not give much idea of the state of each bit in its binary equivalent. Converting a decimal number to its binary equivalent is not a particularly quick or easy process (without the aid of some computerised help anyway). Decimal numbers are consequently rather inconvenient when things must be visualised on a bit by bit basis.

The hexadecimal system gives the best of both worlds in that it takes just a few digits to represent even quite large numbers, and it is in fact slightly better than the decimal numbering system in this respect. On the other hand, it is quite easy to convert hexadecimal numbers to their binary equivalents when the state of each bit must be known. The conversion process is quite simple even with very large numbers. The hexadecimal system is based on the number 16, and there are sixteen single digit numbers. Obviously the numbers we normally use in the decimal system are inadequate for hexadecimal as there are six too few of them. This problem is overcome by augmenting them with the first six digits of the alphabet (A to F). It is from this that the system derives its name. The table given below helps to explain the way in which the hexadecimal system operates.

Decimal	Hexadecimal	Binary
0	0	0000
1	1	0001
2	2	0010
3	3	0011
4	4	0100
5	5	0101
6	6	0110
7	7	0111
8	8	1000
9	9	1001
10	A	1010
11	B	1011
12	C	1100
13	D	1101
14	E	1110
15	F	1111
16	10	10000
17	11	10001
18	12	10010
163	A3	10100011

What makes hexadecimal so convenient is the ease with which multi-digit numbers can be converted into binary equivalents. The reason for this is that each hexadecimal digit represents four binary bits. Take the hexadecimal number A3 in the above table for example. The digit A represents 1010 in binary, and the digit 3 converts to 0011. A3 therefore represents 10100011 in binary. You may find that you can memorise each of the sixteen four bit binary codes represented by hexadecimal digits, but a little mental arithmetic is all that is needed in order to make the conversion if you can not.

The digits in a hexadecimal number represent, working from right to left, the number of units, 16s, 256s, 4096s, 65536s, 1048576s, and 268435450s (approx.). In general computing you are unlikely to use hexadecimal numbers of more than eight digits in length, and mostly you will probably only deal with hexadecimal numbers having four digits or less. When dealing with PIC processors you should not need to use hexadecimal numbers having more than three digits and in most cases you will use only one or two digit numbers.

Conversions
Conversion from hexadecimal to binary is, as we have already seen, fairly straightforward. With a little experience a little mental arithmetic is all that is needed to make this type of conversion. Conversion in the opposite direction is equally simple. It is just a matter of breaking down the binary number into four-bit groups and then converting each group to its corresponding hexadecimal digit.

Conversions that involve decimal numbers are a little more difficult to deal with. The easy way of handling the problem is to use a computer to make the conversion (or possibly a scientific calculator). Most BASICs can provide a hexadecimal to decimal conversion. If the computer accepts hexadecimal numbers with (say) a "&H" prefix to indicate that they are in hexadecimal, then giving the instruction:

PRINT &HXXXX RETURN

where "XXXX" is the hexadecimal number to be converted, should result in the decimal equivalent being printed on the screen. A conversion in the opposite direction might also be possible, and this is most commonly found in the form of a HEX$ function. You may even find that decimal to octal conversion is possible using an OCT$ function (as in Amiga BASIC for instance), although these days such a function would seem to be of largely academic interest.

Bitwise Operations

In computing numbers are not only manipulated using the normal mathematical functions. There are also the "bitwise" operations called "AND", "OR", and "XOR". These compare two binary numbers (literally) bit-by-bit, and the answer produced depends on the combination of 0s and 1s present in each column. ANDing produces a 1 in the answer only if there is a 1 in that column of both the numbers being ANDed. In other words, if a bit is set to 1 in the first number and the second, a 1 is placed in that bit of the answer. Hence the "AND" name of this logic operation. Here is a simple ANDing example

First number	15	00001111
Second number	243	11110011
Answer	3	00000011

The answers obtained from bitwise operations can tend to look a bit random unless you consider what is happening on a bit by bit basis. A common use of the bitwise AND function is when less than all eight bits of a byte must be read. For instance, assume that we wish to know the state of bit 3 of a register or input port. Most computer systems do not provide any direct means of reading just one bit of a port or register. One way around the problem is to use a bitwise AND operation to mask off the unwanted bits. In this case bit 3 represents eight when it is set to logic 1, and so the masking number to use is eight (00000100 in binary). In the answer all the bits except bit 3 must be set to zero, as there is no way they can be set to 1 in both numbers. The situation is different for bit 3, where both bits could be at logic 1 if the second number also has this bit set to 1. The answer therefore reflects the state of bit 3 in the second number, and is eight if this bit is high, or zero if it is at logic 0. The ANDing provides the desired function with, in effect, only the required bit being read.

It is possible to read more than one bit if desired. Just set any bits which must be read to logic 1 in the masking number - set any bits which must be masked off to logic 0 in the masking number. As a couple of examples, to read the least significant nibble a masking number of 15 (00001111 in binary) would be used, and to read the most significant nibble the masking number would be 240 (11110000 in binary).

Bitwise ORing is a similar process to ANDing, but a 1 is placed in a bit of the answer if there is a 1 in that bit of the first number, or the second number, or both. XORing (exclusive ORing) differs from normal (inclusive) ORing in that it will place a 1 in a bit of the answer if there is a 1 in that bit of the first number or the second, but not if there is a 1 in both bits of these numbers. This could reasonably be regarded as the true OR function, but it has been designated the XOR function. The following example shows how these two types of bitwise operation can produce different answers.

First Number	15	00001111
Second Number	85	01010101
ORed Result	95	01011111

First Number	15	00001111
Second Number	85	01010101
XORed Result	90	01011010

The main use of the bitwise OR function is to permit some bits of a register to be altered without changing the states of the other bits. Suppose that you wish to set bits 0 to 3 of a register to 1. You could simply write a value of 15 (00001111) to the register, but if any of bits 4 to 7 were originally set to 1, this would result in them being changed to zero. The way around this is to read the register, and bitwise OR the result with a suitable value. Determining this value is quite straightforward. A one is used in the bits that must be set to one, and a zero is used in the other bits. In our example it is bits 0 to 3 that must be set to one, and bits 3 to 7 that must be left unchanged. This gives a masking number of 15. If you look at the bitwise OR example show previously, where a value of 85 (01010101 in binary) is ORed with 15, you will note that the lower four bits in the answer are all set to one, but the upper four bits remain unchanged. This gives the desired result using just a single instruction.

If you needed to set the lower nibble to zero rather than one, it is a bitwise AND operation that would be used. Use a one in any bits that must be left unaltered, and a zero in bits that must be zero. A value of 240 (11110000) would therefore be used to set the four least significant bits to zero, as shown in this example.

Number In Register	85	01010101
Masking Number	240	11110000
Answer	80	01010000

The bitwise XOR function perhaps has fewer practical uses than the AND and OR functions, when dealing with do-it-yourself add-ons anyway. It is probably the favourite bitwise operation for those involved in graphics. Using an XOR instruction it is possible to complement the bits in a byte (change the 1s to 0s and vice versa) by XORing the byte with 255 (11111111 in binary).

BASIC

Although we live in the days of 32-bit programming languages and graphical user interfaces, most programming for user add-ons is still done with either Q BASIC, or its predecessor GW BASIC. One reason for this is undoubtedly that Q BASIC is supplied free with Windows 95/98, and GW BASIC was supplied as part of the MS/DOS operating system. Q BASIC is not actually included as part of a standard Windows 95 or 98 installation, but it is present on the CD-ROM if you seek it out. It is in the :\tools\oldmsdos subdirectory of my Windows 98 CD-ROM for example. Many PC do-it-yourself add-ons do not require particularly complex software, and Q BASIC or GW BASIC is adequate for the purpose. There are drawbacks to these "free" BASIC languages, one of which is that they run under MS/DOS, although they seem to run well enough under the Windows 95/ 98 "MS/DOS Prompt". Another consideration is that they are both interpreted languages and not compilers. This means that they do not produce stand-alone programs. A GW BASIC or Q BASIC program will only run from within one or other of these programming languages. This is not such a major drawback, since both programs are very small by current standards. In fact one way of handling things is to put GW BASIC or Q BASIC onto an MS/DOS floppy boot disc, and to boot from this when you want to use or produce BASIC programs. A high-density disc has sufficient storage space for BASIC plus a number of your programs.

Another drawback of an interpreted language is that it is relatively slow. A compiler converts your code into a stand-alone .exe program file that should run very fast. Some compilers are more efficient than others, and results are not usually equal to those obtained by a good programmer using assembly language. However, any reasonably good compiler should produce software that runs very quickly on a modern PC. An interpreted language takes a section of code, converts it into the corresponding machine code, and then runs it. It then moves on to the next section of code and repeats the process. Because the process of interpreting the code occurs at run-time it seriously slows things down. In fact an interpreted program will typically run something like ten to one hundred time slower than a compiled equivalent, and in some cases even slower than this. There is actually a sort of Q BASIC compiler called Quick BASIC, but this does not seem to be available any more. If you can locate a copy it is well worthwhile giving it a try.

Anyway, if you wish to try your hand at producing programs for PC projects, GW BASIC and Q BASIC probably represent the best starting points because they are effectively free. You can therefore produce some initial programs and experiment with PC add-ons without having to risk a substantial outlay on a programming language. If you should find them to be inadequate for your purposes you can always move on to something more potent. GW BASIC and Q BASIC are largely compatible incidentally, and most programs written for one will run without modification under the other. They have different user interfaces, with Q BASIC having a slightly more modern approach to things. Q BASIC does not require line numbers, although it will use them if they are included in a program. GW BASIC does require line numbers, and will therefore only work with Q BASIC programs that include them.

INs and Outs

With GW and Q BASIC the ports are accessed using the OUT instruction and the INP function. To set the data lines of printer port one at a value of 250 this instruction would therefore be used:

OUT &H378,250

The "&H" ahead of the address indicates that it is a hexadecimal number, and it seems to be the convention to use hexadecimal for addresses when using GW BASIC or Q BASIC. The instruction will also work using the address in decimal (i.e. OUT 888,250). The value written to the port can be a numeric variable if necessary (e.g. OUT &H378,TEMP).

Reading the port is equally easy, and the reading would normally be placed in a variable so that it can then be manipulated in the desired fashion. In this example the returned value is simply printed on the screen.

165

```
10 OUT &H37A,32
20 X = INP(&H378)
30 PRINT X
```

The first line writes a value of 32 to the port's handshake output register, which sets the data lines to the input mode. The next line reads the data lines and places the result in variable "X". Finally, the contents of "X" are printed on the screen at the current cursor position. GW BASIC and Q BASIC are very easy-going when it comes to variables, and you can simply make them up as you go along. There is no need to declare variables at the beginning of the program. Also, there is no need to convert a numeric variable to a string prior to printing it on the screen. It is automatically converted into the corresponding string of figures.

Windows
The generally accepted wisdom is that Windows programming languages do not permit direct accessing of the ports, but this is not totally true. Modern Windows programming languages do not include direct port access as a standard feature, but it can actually be added via an add-on. Of course, this is only feasible in practice if you can find a ready-made add-on or can produce one for yourself. There are a couple of other options available, and one of these is to use Borland's C++ 4.5 to compile a standard MS/DOS C++ program. In the MS/DOS versions of C++ it is usually possible to access the ports using "inp" and "out". Borland's C++ 4.5 supports these instructions, and will compile MS/DOS C++ programs into Windows programs. In fact you end up with what is still basically the original MS/DOS program, but it runs under Windows in its own window.

This could be more convenient than running the MS/DOS original via the Windows "MS/DOS Prompt" option or rebooting in MS/DOS mode, but it is not really a big step forward from either of these. Also, you have to bear in mind that the program produced is a 16-bit Windows type. This should work properly if run under Windows 3.1, 95, or 98, but would presumably fail to work with Windows NT. Borland C++ 4.5 is no longer available, but I believe that it is included with version 5 in order to provide users with a means of producing 16-bit Windows programs. It has also been given away free with some computer magazines, but there are some restrictions on the use of the "free" version. These should not be a problem if you are only using the program for personal use, but any commercial or formal educational use seems to be prohibited.

Delphi
There is a better solution to producing Windows programs for your projects in the form of Delphi, which is another Borland product. Unfortunately, only the original version of Delphi (now usually referred to as Delphi 1) supports direct port access. Delphi 1 produces 16-bit Windows programs, but like C++ 4.5 programs, these should run perfectly well under Windows 95 or 98. As far as I am aware, Delphi 1 is no longer available as a separate product, but it was certainly included with Delphi 2 and 3 to provide a means of producing 16-bit programs. At the time of writing this, Delphi has moved on to version 4, and the specification for this version still includes 16-bit compatibility so it presumably includes version 1. However, it would be as well to check this point before buying version 4 in order to obtain the original Delphi program. Delphi 1 has also been given away free with some computer magazines, but like the "free" version of C++ 4.5 there are some restrictions on its use.

So why is Delphi better than using C++ version 4.5, or simply sticking with GW BASIC, etc? Delphi is a "visual" programming language (like Visual BASIC) that makes it easy to produce standard Windows style programs, complete with control buttons, dialogue boxes, scroll-bars, and all the familiar Windows gadgets. There is insufficient space available here for in-depth coverage of Delphi programming, which seems to require a minimum of about 3000 pages! We will only consider the basics of getting Delphi to directly access the ports. In order to produce Delphi programs for most projects you do not need to be an expert in this programming language, so once you have digested a few fundamentals of Delphi programming it should not be too difficult to get your projects operating via a Windows environment.

Visual Programming
If you are only familiar with traditional programming languages such as GW BASIC it is only fair to point out that Delphi and other visual languages are a rather different concept. You still have to do some traditional programming with variables, loops, and so on, but much of the code is produced without the need for any programming. Delphi is based on the Pascal programming language, and Object Pascal is the language at the heart of the system. This is apparently based on Borland's Turbo Pascal programming language. Anyone who is familiar with the Pascal programming should have little difficulty in learning to use any version of Delphi.

So just how does visual programming differ from the traditional approach? The differences will start to become apparent as soon as Delphi is first run. Unusually, at start-up there are four windows open (Figure 5.1). The window at the top of the screen has the usual menu bar, etc., and could be regarded as the main program window. The majority of the section below the menu bar contains the component palette. This makes it easy to add all manner of objects into your programs, including buttons, pull-down menus, and labels. What is termed the form is situated below the component palette, and the form is where you design the visual appearance of you finished program. The size of the form determines the starting size of the program window, and if you place a button in the bottom left hand corner of the form, a button will appear in exactly the same place in the program window. The form has a grid of dots to help you place components accurately, but these are not shown in the program window. You can actually have more than one form per program,

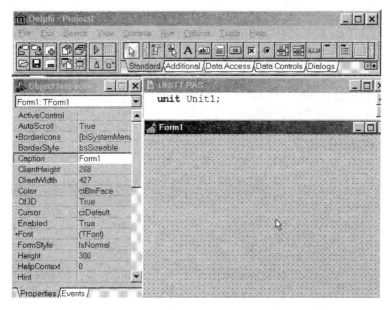

Fig.5.1   At start-up Delphi has four windows open

but we will settle for just one form in the demonstration programs featured here.

The object inspector occupies the left-hand portion of the screen. This provides control over the form and the components contained within it. You can adjust the size and position of objects by dragging them or by entering the relevant figures into the object inspector. The object inspector also provides control over colours, text fonts and sizes, and a great deal else. Largely hidden behind the form you will find the code window, which is where the program code is entered. However, with the visual programming method the amount of traditional program writing required is sometimes quite small. A lot of the program code is produced simply by dropping buttons, etc., onto the form and adjusting parameters. This is not to say that no programming is required. You must enter some code for a button

169

or operating it will have no effect. In advanced applications a great deal of "hand written" code will be required, but the visual approach takes much of the hard work out of Windows programming. It also has to be pointed out that the structure of programs is radically different to traditional programming. If you are used to using an old style programming language such as GW BASIC you have to drastically change your ways of thinking in order to properly utilize a visual programming language.

Outputting Data

Delphi provides access to the ports via the port and portw functions. These are respectively used for eight and 16-bit operations, and here we will only consider eight-bit port accesses. Depending on the syntax used, port can be used to read from a port or write data to it. This program line would write a value of 123 to printer port one at address 888 (decimal).

Port[888] := 123;

Note that the port address is contained in square brackets, and not the ordinary brackets used with the BASIC OUT instruction. Also note that in this context the equals sign must be preceded by a colon, and that all normal Pascal program lines end with a semicolon. As a simple test of writing to a port select the button component in the component palette, and click the mouse at two points on the form. This will drop two buttons onto the form. Select one of these and change its caption to "85". Then double-click on the button to bring up the code window, which will contain the basic framework for your program. Your code for the button goes between the words "begin" and "end", and only this line of code has to be added:

Port[888] := 85;

Next click on the other button to select it and use the object inspector to change its caption to "170". Then double-click on the button and add this program line in the code window between "begin" and "end".

Port[888] := 170;

You can now save this project and the code, and then select the "Compile" option from the "Compile" menu to produce a stand-alone program file that can be run under Windows 3.1, 95, or 98. Alternatively, if you want to try out the program without compiling it select "Run" from the "Run" menu and this will run the program from within Delphi. Either way you should get a program window the same size as the form, complete with the two captioned buttons. Pressing the "85" button will output the binary code 01010101 to printer port one. Pressing the "170" button outputs the binary code 10101010 to the port. Of course, a variable can be used instead of a number in the Port instruction, but it must be a variable of a suitable type such as a byte or integer variable.

Reading
Reading a port requires the Port instruction to be used in this form:

Variable := Port[Address];

Delphi requires variables to be declared before they are used in the program, and they can not simply be made up as you go along. Also, you have to be careful that you only use variables in an appropriate fashion. With BASIC you can read a port and then print the returned value on the screen with a minimum of fuss. With Delphi matters are slightly more difficult because the value read from the port must be placed in an integer or byte variable, but writing text to the screen requires a string variable. This requires a type conversion from a byte or integer to a string variable before the returned value can be printed. In order to set up the byte and string variables these two lines could be added in the code window under the "var" heading:

```
Reading : Byte;
S : String;
```

This sets "Reading" as a byte variable, and this would be used to store the value returned from the port. Variable "S" is a string variable, and would be used to hold the text converted from "Reading". These program lines could be assigned to a button, and would print the value returned from printer port one each time the button was clicked. Note that this will only work if printer port one is a bidirectional type.

```
Port[890] := 32;
Reading := Port[888];
Str(Reading, S);
Canvas.TextOut (50,50, '      ');
Canvas.TextOut (50,50, S);
```

The first line outputs a value of 32 to the port to set it to the input mode. The next line then reads the port's data register and places the result in the variable called "Reading". The third line takes the value contained in "Reading" and converts it into the corresponding text string, which is placed in variable "S". Line four writes a series of spaces to the form, and this is done to blank any previous reading that is displayed. Finally, the string contain in "S" is printed on the form, 50 pixels down and 50 pixels in from the top left-hand corner of the form. The value on the screen is updated each time the button is clicked.

Time After Time
Delphi provides facilities that are potentially very useful when writing software for your add-ons. The next program demonstrates two of these, which are the interval timer component and the graphics facilities. By default the timer executes its section of code every second, but the interval can be altered by the user and has a resolution of one millisecond. The timer component can be found in the component palette but it is not in the "Standard" set shown at start-up. If you click

172

on the "System" tab of the component palette the timer button will be displayed. If you click on this and then click anywhere on the form the timer object will be installed in the form. This is not a visual component, and the timer icon will not appear in the program window when the program is run. The icon appears on the form to remind you that it is in use, and to provide you with access to its properties. Double-click on the timer icon to bring up the code window and then add this code between "begin" and "end".

```
Timer1.Interval := 250;
Canvas.TextOut (55, 0, '0');
Canvas.TextOut (55, 50, '50');
Canvas.TextOut (55, 100, '100');
Canvas.TextOut (55, 150, '150');
Canvas.TextOut (55, 200, '200');
Canvas.TextOut (55, 250, '250');
port[890] := 32;
Reading := port[888];
Form1.Canvas.FillRect (Rect (0, 0, 50, 300));
Form1.Canvas.Pen.Width := 5;
Canvas.MoveTo (25, 0);
Canvas.LineTo (25, Reading);
```

Also, under the "var" heading add this line:

Reading : Byte;

The purpose of the program is to produce a simple bargraph display that shows the values returned from the printer port, which must be a bidirectional type. The first line of the program sets the timer interval at 250 milliseconds, but you can use any valid value here. Bear in mind that the screen only updates at around 50 to 75 times per second, and that there is no point in using very low interval values. A series of six program lines then print a scale of values for the bargraph. Next the port is set to the input mode and then the value read from the port is stored

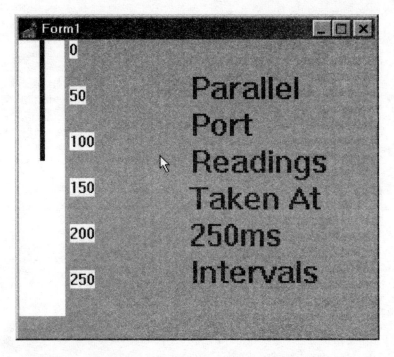

Fig.5.2 A screen-dump showing the bargraph program in operation

in variable called "Reading". Then a rectangle is drawn in the default colour (white), and this produces a panel for the bargraph to operate in. It also blanks out the previous reading so that the new one can be displayed properly. The next three lines actually draw the line of the bargraph. First the pen width is increased from the default value of one pixel to five pixels so that the bargraph is easier to see and read. The MoveTo instruction moves the pen to the specified screen co-ordinates but does not actually draw anything on the screen. Finally, the LineTo instruction actually draws the line, with variable "Reading" defining how far down the screen the line is drawn. If you add a label to describe the function of the program, then compile and run it, you should end up with something along the lines of Figure 5.2.

I am not sure if you can achieve anything using Delphi that could not also be achieved using BASIC, but it is clearly possible to do many things much more easily using Delphi. Also, the fact that it produces stand-alone programs that run under Windows 3.1, 95 or 98 make it an attractive proposition for those who no longer use MS/DOS. Although Delphi is not the fastest programming language around, it is a compiled language and on any reasonably modern PC it certainly runs at a rate that is fast enough for the vast majority of applications.

Appendix

TAPPING OFF POWER

Obtaining power from a PC project is not usually difficult if the unit is in the form of an internal expansion card. The ISA expansion ports give access to the supply rails of the PC, and these will normally be sufficient to power your add-on devices. Of course, there is a limit to the amount of power that can be safely tapped off, but there should be no difficulty in tapping off an amp or so from the +5-volt supply. The +12 volt supply can also provide quite hefty currents if required, but note that this supply is not usually well regulated, and it can contain massive amounts of noise. The negative supplies usually have quite modest maximum output current ratings, but it is unlikely that your add-ons will actually need to use them at all.

For an add-on that connects to a serial or parallel port things are somewhat trickier. Neither of these ports have any form of power supply output. If your add-on requires anything other than a straightforward +5-volt supply it is probably best to provide it with its own battery supply or a suitable mains power supply unit. If only a +5-volt supply is needed it is usually better to tap off the supply from one of the PC's ports that does provide a supply output. With most PCs there are two options. The easiest of these is to take power from the game port, although not all PCs actually have one of these. In older PCs a multifunction input/output card generally provides this port, but in recent models it is usually to be found on the sound card. In the case of a sound card game port it is invariably a combined MIDI and game port, but it still provides +5 volt outputs. The game port connector on the PC is a 15 way female D type, and you therefore need a 15 way male D connector to make the connection to this port. The +5-volt supply can be obtained from pin 1, as in the top drawing of Figure 6.1.

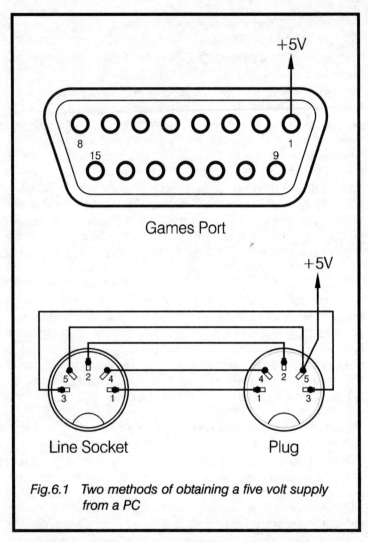

+5V

+5V

Games Port

Line Socket

Plug

Fig.6.1 Two methods of obtaining a five volt supply from a PC

The alternative is to use the keyboard port. There is a slight complication here in that it is necessary to make up a simple adapter in order to enable power to be tapped off while still using the keyboard. Basically all you need is a 5-way 180-degree

DIN line socket and a matching plug. The two are wired together as shown in the lower drawing of Figure 6.1, using a short piece of any normal 5-way cable (ribbon, screened, etc.). An additional lead connected to pin 5 of the plug provides the +5-volt supply. The plug connects to the keyboard port of the computer and the keyboard connects to the line socket.

With some modern PCs there is actually a third alternative, which is to use the USB port. At present relatively few PCs are equipped with this type of port, and many of those which have this facility on the motherboard do not actually have the necessary connector fitted at the rear of the computer. However, if your PC does have a USB port it would be worthwhile investigating the possibility of using this as a +5-volt power source.

Index

16550 143
5-volt supply 177
8255 62

A
ADC0844 72
address bus 14
address decoder 42
address enable 15
address range 38
AEN 15
ALE 15
analogue to digital 72
AND 48
ASCII 138

B
BASIC 163
baud rate 124
BCD 157
bidirectional 116
binary 155
BIOS 7
bitwise 161
brackets 26

C
C++ 166
Centronics 41
clock 17
control bus 15
CTS 137

D
D connector 86
D type 59
data bus 14
DCE 138
decode 35